GCSE OCR Gateway
Chemistry
Higher Revision Guide

This book is for anyone doing **GCSE OCR Gateway Chemistry** at higher level.
It covers everything you'll need for your year 10 and 11 exams.

GCSE Science is all about **understanding how science works**.
And not only that — understanding it well enough to be able to **question**
what you hear on TV and read in the papers.

But you can't do that without a fair chunk of **background knowledge**. Hmm, tricky.

Happily this CGP book includes all the **science facts** you need to learn,
and shows you how they work in the **real world**. And in true CGP style,
we've explained it all as **clearly and concisely** as possible.

It's also got some daft bits in to try and make the whole
experience at least vaguely entertaining for you.

What CGP is all about

Our sole aim here at CGP is to produce the highest
quality books — carefully written, immaculately presented
and dangerously close to being funny.

Then we work our socks off to get them
out to you — at the cheapest possible prices.

Contents

MODULE C4 — THE PERIODIC TABLE

MODULE C5 — HOW MUCH?

MODULE C6 — CHEMISTRY OUT THERE

Published by CGP

From original material by Richard Parsons.

Editors:
Katie Braid, Mary Falkner, Ben Fletcher, David Hickinson, Helen Ronan.

Contributors:
Mike Bossart, Lucy Muncaster.

ISBN: 978 1 84762 621 9

With thanks to Katherine Craig, Barrie Crowther, Philip Dobson and Hayley Thompson
for the proofreading.
With thanks to Laura Stoney for the copyright research.

GORE-TEX®, GORE®, and designs are registered trademarks of W.L. Gore and Associates.
This book contains copyrighted material reproduced with the permission of W.L. Gore and Associates.
Copyright 2011 W.L. Gore and Associates.

Groovy website: www.cgpbooks.co.uk

Printed by Elanders Ltd, Newcastle upon Tyne.
Jolly bits of clipart from CorelDRAW®

Photocopying — it's dull, grey and sometimes a bit naughty. Luckily, it's dead cheap, easy and quick to order
more copies of this book from CGP — just call us on 0870 750 1242. Phew!

The Scientific Process

You need to know a few things about how the world of science works — both for your <u>exams</u> and your <u>controlled assessment</u>. Investigate these next few pages and you'll be laughing all day long on results day.

Scientists Come Up with Hypotheses — Then Test Them

1) Scientists try to <u>explain</u> things. Everything.

2) They start by <u>observing</u> or <u>thinking about</u> something they don't understand — it could be anything, e.g. planets in the sky, a person suffering from an illness, what matter is made of... anything.

3) Then, using what they already know (plus a bit of insight), they come up with a <u>hypothesis</u> — a possible <u>explanation</u> for what they've observed.

4) The next step is to <u>test</u> whether the hypothesis might be <u>right or not</u> — this involves <u>gathering evidence</u> (i.e. <u>data</u> from <u>investigations</u>).

About 100 years ago, we thought atoms looked like this.

5) To gather evidence the scientist uses the hypothesis to make a <u>prediction</u> — a statement based on the hypothesis that can be <u>tested</u> by carrying out <u>experiments</u>.

6) If the results from the experiments match the prediction, then the scientist can be <u>more confident</u> that the hypothesis is <u>correct</u>. This <u>doesn't</u> mean the hypothesis is <u>true</u> though — other predictions based on the hypothesis might turn out to be <u>wrong</u>.

Scientists Work Together to Test Hypotheses

1) Different scientists can look at the <u>same evidence</u> and interpret it in <u>different ways</u>. That's why scientists usually work in <u>teams</u> — they can share their <u>different ideas</u> on how to interpret the data they find.

Then we thought they looked like this.

2) Once a team has come up with (and tested) a hypothesis they all agree with, they'll present their work to the scientific community through <u>journals</u> and <u>scientific conferences</u> so it can be judged — this is called the <u>peer review</u> process.

3) Other scientists then <u>check</u> the team's results (by trying to <u>replicate</u> them) and carry out their own experiments to <u>collect more evidence</u>.

4) If all the experiments in the world back up the hypothesis, scientists start to have a lot of <u>confidence</u> in it.

5) However, if another scientist does an experiment and the results <u>don't</u> fit with the hypothesis (and other scientists can <u>replicate</u> these results), then the hypothesis is in trouble. When this happens, scientists have to come up with a new hypothesis (maybe a <u>modification</u> of the old explanation, or maybe a completely <u>new</u> one).

Scientific Ideas Change as New Evidence is Found

1) Scientific explanations are <u>provisional</u> because they only explain the evidence that's <u>currently available</u> — new evidence may come up that can't be explained.

2) This means that scientific explanations <u>never</u> become hard and fast, totally indisputable <u>fact</u>. As <u>new evidence</u> is found (or new ways of <u>interpreting</u> existing evidence are found), hypotheses can <u>change</u> or be <u>replaced</u>.

And then we thought they looked like this.

3) Sometimes, an <u>unexpected observation</u> or <u>result</u> will suddenly throw a hypothesis into doubt and further experiments will need to be carried out. This can lead to new developments that <u>increase</u> our <u>understanding</u> of science.

You expect me to believe that — then show me the evidence...

If scientists think something is true, they need to produce evidence to convince others — it's all part of <u>testing a hypothesis</u>. One hypothesis might survive these tests, while others won't — it's how things progress. And along the way some hypotheses will be disproved — i.e. shown not to be true.

Scientific Information and Development

Sadly, science isn't always as straightforward as you might think. Here are a few reasons why...

Scientific Information Isn't Always Very Good Quality

1) Scientific information can be presented by a person who is biased.

2) When a person is biased, it means that they favour a particular interpretation of the evidence for a reason that's incorrect or unrelated to the scientific information. Bias can be intentional or unintentional.

3) A person who is intentionally biased might misrepresent the evidence — give the true facts, but present them in a way that makes them misleading. This might be to persuade you to agree with them...

EXAMPLE

Scientists say 1 in 2 people are of above average weight

Sounds like we're a nation of fatties. It's a scientific analysis of the facts, and almost certainly true.

But an average is a kind of 'middle value' of all your data. Some readings are higher than average (about half of them, usually). Others will be lower than average (the other half).

So the above headline (which made it sound like we should all lose weight) could just as accurately say:

Scientists say 1 in 2 people are of below average weight

4) A person who is intentionally biased might also give scientific information without any evidence to back it up. This might be because there's no evidence to support what they're saying, or it could be that the person is just ignoring the evidence that exists (e.g. because it contradicts what they're saying).

5) Information that isn't backed up with any evidence could just be an opinion — you've got no way of telling whether it's true or not.

Society Influences the Development of Science

1) The question of whether something is morally or ethically right or wrong can't be answered by experiments — there is no "right" or "wrong" answer.

2) The best we can do is get a consensus from society — a judgement that most people are more or less happy to live by. Science can provide more information to help people make this judgement, and the judgement might change over time. But in the end it's up to people and their conscience.

3) In an ideal world, the best decision about any moral or ethical dilemma would have the best outcome for the majority of people involved.

Other Factors Can Affect Scientific Development Too

Economic factors:
- Companies very often won't pay for research unless there's likely to be a profit in it.
- Society can't always afford to do things scientists recommend (e.g. investing heavily in alternative energy sources) without cutting back elsewhere.

Social factors: Decisions based on scientific evidence affect people — e.g. should fossil fuels be taxed more highly (to invest in alternative energy)? Should alcohol be banned (to prevent health problems)? Would the effect on people's lifestyles be acceptable...?

Cultural factors: Cultural feelings can sometimes affect whether research is carried out or given funding, e.g. some people are against research which involves animal testing.

It's a scientific fact that the Moon's made of cheese...

Whenever you're given any kind of scientific information just stop for a second and ask yourself how convincing it really is — think about the evidence that's been used (if any) and the way that the information's been presented.

Coo...

This is a page about irreve...
substance changes, and it...

Some Foods Have...

There are loads of differe...
grilling and cooking in an...

1) Many foods have a be...
2) Some foods are easie...
3) The high temperatures...
   that cause disease —...
4) Some foods are poiso...
   contain a poison that'...

Cooking Causes...

Cooking food produces n...
change has taken place.
The cooking process is ir...

e.g. Eggs and M...

e.g. Potatoes...

Baking Powder...

1) When you heat bakin...
2) Thermal decompositio...
   Many thermal decom...
   from a lot of reactio...
3) Baking powder conta...
   You need to know th...

   The word equation...
   The symbol equatio...

4) Baking powder is us...
5) You can check that i...
   carbon dioxide that I...
   formed by using a cl...

You'll need to lea...

Cooking is a kind of chemis...
The changes are irreversible...

Planning Investigations

That's all the dull stuff about the world of science over — now onto the hands-on part. The next few pages show how practical investigations should be carried out — by both professional scientists and you.

To Make an Investigation a Fair Test You Have to Control the Variables

An important part of planning an investigation is making sure it's a fair test.

1) In a lab experiment you usually change one variable and measure how it affects the other variable.

> EXAMPLE: you might change only the temperature of a chemical reaction and measure how this affects the rate of reaction.

2) To make it a fair test everything else that could affect the results should stay the same (otherwise you can't tell if the thing that's being changed is affecting the results or not — the data won't be reliable).

> EXAMPLE continued: you need to keep the concentration of the reactants the same, otherwise you won't know if any change in the rate of reaction is caused by the change in temperature, or a difference in reactant concentration.

3) The variable that you change is called the independent variable.
4) The variable that's measured is called the dependent variable.
5) The variables that you keep the same are called control variables.
6) Because you can't always control all the variables, you often need to use a control experiment — an experiment that's kept under the same conditions as the rest of the investigation, but doesn't have anything done to it. This is so that you can see what happens when you don't change anything at all.

> EXAMPLE continued:
> Independent = temperature
> Dependent = rate of reaction
> Control = reactant concentration

The Equipment Used has to be Right for the Job

1) The measuring equipment you use has to be sensitive enough to accurately measure the chemicals you're using, e.g. if you need to measure out 11 ml of a liquid, you'll need to use a measuring cylinder that can measure to 1 ml, not 5 or 10 ml.
2) The smallest change a measuring instrument can detect is called its RESOLUTION. E.g. some mass balances have a resolution of 1 g and some have a resolution of 0.1 g.
3) You should also be able to explain why you've chosen each bit of kit.

Experiments Must be Safe

1) Part of planning an investigation is making sure that it's safe.
2) There are lots of hazards you could be faced with during an investigation, e.g. radiation, electricity, gas, chemicals and fire.
3) You should always make sure that you identify all the hazards that you might encounter.
4) You should also come up with ways of reducing the risks from the hazards you've identified.
5) One way of doing this is to carry out a risk assessment:

> For an experiment involving a Bunsen burner, the risk assessment might be something like this:

> Hazard: Bunsen burner is a fire risk.
> Precautions:
> • Keep flammable chemicals away from the Bunsen.
> • Never leave the Bunsen unattended when lit.
> • Always turn on the yellow safety flame when not in use.

Hazard: revision boredom. Precaution: use CGP books

Wow, all this even before you've started the investigation — it really does make them run more smoothly though.

All sorts of natural a
Emulsifiers are additi

Additives Ma

Additives are added

1) Food colours n
2) Flavour enhanc
3) Antioxidants he
4) Emulsifiers help
   salad cream an

Emulsifiers H

1) You can mix an
2) Emulsions are r
3) Oil and water na
   don't "want" to
4) Mayonnaise, lov
5) Emulsifiers are r
   and another par
6) The bit that's at
   to oil is called h

7) The hydrophilic
8) The hydrophobi
9) When you shake
   with a bit of em
   droplets, surrou
   emulsifier... wit
   facing outwards
10) Other oil droplet
    hydrophilic bit o
    water molecules
    emulsion won't

Add me to food

Some people don't like
make additive-free pro
— the words, diagrams

Solutions

Solutions are all around you — e.g. sea water, bath salts... And inside you even — e.g. instant coffee...

A Solution is a Mixture of Solvent and Solute

When you add a solid (the solute) to a liquid (the solvent) the bonds holding the solute molecules together sometimes break and the molecules then mix with the molecules in the liquid — forming a solution. This is called dissolving. Whether the bonds break depends on how strong the attractions are between the molecules within each substance and how strong the attractions are between the two substances.

Here's some definitions you need to know: *Learn this definition of a solution — they might ask you for it in the exam.*

1) Solution – is a mixture of a solute and a solvent that does not separate out.
2) Solute – is the substance being dissolved.
3) Solvent – is the liquid it's dissolving into.
4) Soluble – means it will dissolve.
5) Insoluble – means it will **NOT** dissolve.
6) Solubility – a measure of how much will dissolve.

E.g. brine is a solution of salt and water — if you evaporated off the solvent (the water), you'd see the solute (the salt) again.

Water is a very common solvent.

Nail Varnish is Insoluble in Water...

Nail varnish doesn't dissolve in water. This is for two reasons:

1) The molecules of nail varnish are strongly attracted to each other. This attraction is stronger than the attraction between the nail varnish molecules and the water molecules.
2) The molecules of water are strongly attracted to each other. This attraction is stronger than the attraction between the water molecules and the nail varnish molecules.

Because the two substances are more attracted to themselves than each other, they don't form a solution.

...but Soluble in Acetone

Nail varnish dissolves in acetone — more commonly known as nail varnish remover. This is because the attraction between acetone molecules and nail varnish molecules is stronger than the attractions holding the two substances together.

So the solubility of a substance depends on the solvent used.

Acetone is also called propanone.

Lots of Things are Solvents

Alcohols and esters can be used as solvents, and so can lots of other weird and wacky organic molecules. Ability to dissolve a solute isn't the only consideration though... some solvents are horribly poisonous.

Example: Mothballs are made of a substance called naphthalene. Imagine you've trodden a mothball into your carpet. Choose one of the solvents from the table to clean it up.

Solvent	Solubility of naphthalene	Boiling point	Other properties
water	0 g/100 g	100 °C	safe
methanol	9.7 g/100 g	65 °C	flammable
ethyl acetate	18.5 g/100 g	77 °C	flammable
dichloromethane	25.0 g/100 g	40 °C	extremely toxic

Looking at the data, water wouldn't be a good choice because it doesn't dissolve the naphthalene. Dichloromethane would dissolve it easily, but it's very toxic. Of the two solvents left, ethyl acetate dissolves more naphthalene (so you won't need as much). Ethyl acetate is best (just don't set light to it).

Learn this page, it's the only solution...

If you ever spill bright pink nail varnish (or any other colour for that matter) on your carpet, go easy with the nail varnish remover. If you use too much, the nail varnish dissolves in the remover, forming a solution which can go everywhere — and you end up with an enormous bright pink stain... aaagh.

Paints and Pigments

You might just think of paint as brightly coloured stuff — but there's a lot of chemistry that goes into making your bedroom walls lime green.

Pigments Give Paints Their Colours

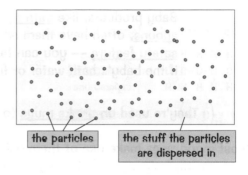

1) Paint usually contains the following bits: solvent, binding medium and pigment.

2) The pigment gives the paint its colour.

3) The binding medium is a liquid that carries the pigment bits and holds them together. When the binding medium goes solid it sticks the pigments to the surface you've painted.

4) The solvent is the stuff that thins the paint and makes it easier to spread.

Paints are Colloids

1) A colloid consists of really tiny particles of one kind of stuff dispersed in (mixed in with) another kind of stuff. They're mixed in, but not dissolved.

2) The particles can be bits of solid, droplets of liquid or bubbles of gas.

3) Colloids don't separate out because the particles are so small. They don't settle out at the bottom.

4) A paint is a colloid where particles of a pigment (usually a solid) are dispersed through a liquid.

the particles | the stuff the particles are dispersed in

Some Paints are Water-based and Some are Oil-based

When you're painting (whether it's a bedroom wall or a work of art) you usually apply paint in a thin layer. The paint dries as the solvent evaporates. (A thin layer dries a heck of a lot quicker than a thick layer.)

Depending on the type of job you're doing, you might choose a water-based paint or an oil-based paint.

1) Emulsion paints are water-based. The solvent used in these paints is water, and the binding medium is usually an acrylic or vinyl acetate polymer.

2) A water-based emulsion dries when the solvent evaporates, leaving behind the binder and pigment as a thin solid film. A thin layer of emulsion paint dries quite quickly.

3) Emulsion paints are fast-drying and don't produce harmful fumes — so they're ideal for painting things like inside walls.

1) Traditional gloss paint and artists' oil paints are oil-based. This time, the binding material is oil, and the solvent is an organic compound that'll dissolve oil.

2) Oil paints dry in two stages. First the solvent evaporates, and then the oil is oxidised by oxygen in the air before it turns solid. (So they tend to take longer to dry than water-based paints.)

3) Oil paints are glossy, waterproof and hard-wearing, but the solvents used to make them often produce harmful fumes. They're best used for painting things like outside doors and metalwork.

Some modern gloss paints are water-based.

The world was black and white before the 1950s — I saw it on TV...

There are heaps of different types of paint — and some are more suitable for certain jobs than others. Like if you're repainting your car, watercolours are definitely not the way to go. And likewise if you painted your little sister's face with gloss paint, your mum would probably ground you for a year.

Polymers and Their Uses

Plastics are fantastically useful. You can make novelty football pencil sharpeners and all sorts.

Polymers' Properties Decide What They're Used For

Different polymers have different physical properties — some are stronger, some are stretchier, some are more easily moulded, and so on. These different physical properties make them suited for different uses.

- Strong, rigid polymers such as high density polyethene are used to make plastic milk bottles.
- Light, stretchable polymers such as low density polyethene are used for plastic bags and squeezy bottles. Low density polyethene has a low melting point, so it's no good for anything that'll get very hot.
- PVC is strong and durable, and it can be made either rigid or stretchy. The rigid kind is used to make window frames and piping. The stretchy kind is used to make synthetic leather.
- Polystyrene foam is used in packaging to protect breakable things, and it's used to make disposable coffee cups (the trapped air in the foam makes it a brilliant thermal insulator).

Polymers are Often Used to Make Clothes

1) Nylon is a synthetic polymer often used to make clothes. Fabrics made from nylon are not waterproof on their own, but can be coated with polyurethane to make tough, hard-wearing and waterproof outdoor clothing which also keeps UV light out.

2) One big problem is that the polyurethane coating doesn't let water vapour pass through it. So if you get a bit hot (or do a bit of exercise), sweat condenses on the inside. This makes skin and clothes get wet and uncomfortable — the material isn't breathable.

3) Some fabrics, e.g. GORE-TEX® products, have all the useful properties of nylon/polyurethane ones, but are also breathable. If you sweat in breathable material, water vapour can escape — so no condensation.

1) GORE-TEX® fabrics are made by laminating a thin film of a plastic called expanded PTFE onto a layer of another fabric, such as polyester or nylon. This makes the PTFE sturdier.

2) The PTFE film has tiny holes which let water vapour through — so it's breathable. But it's waterproof, since the holes aren't big enough to let big water droplets through and the PTFE repels liquid water.

nylon / polyester

PTFE film

water molecules pass through the tiny holes

sweat evaporates from skin (as water vapour)

raindrop too big to get through holes

3) This material is great for outdoorsy types — they can hike without getting rained on or soaked in sweat.

Non-biodegradable Plastics Cause Disposal Problems

1) Most polymers aren't "biodegradable" — they're not broken down by micro-organisms, so they don't rot. This property is actually kind of useful until it's time to get rid of your plastic.

2) It's difficult to get rid of plastics — if you bury them in a landfill site, they'll still be there years later. Landfill sites fill up quickly, and they're a waste of land. And a waste of plastic.

3) When plastics are burnt, some of them release gases such as acidic sulfur dioxide and poisonous hydrogen chloride and hydrogen cyanide. So burning's out, really. Plus it's a waste of plastic.

4) The best thing is to reuse plastics as many times as possible and then recycle them if you can. Sorting out lots of different plastics for recycling is difficult and expensive, though.

5) Chemists are working on a variety of ideas to produce polymers that biodegrade or dissolve — that way any plastic that is thrown away breaks down or dissolves rather than sitting there in landfill for ages.

Disposal problems — you should go and see a doctor...

If you're making a product, you need to pick your plastic carefully. It's no good trying to make a kettle out of a plastic that melts at 50 °C — you'll end up with a messy kitchen, a burnt hand and no cuppa. You'd also have a bit of difficulty trying to wear clothes made of brittle, un-bendy plastic.

Hydrocarbons — Alkanes

Hydrocarbons look like simple enough chemicals — just carbon and hydrogen. But different types of hydrocarbon molecules can have all sorts of different properties — and we use them for loads of things.

Hydrocarbons Only Contain Hydrogen and Carbon Atoms

A hydrocarbon is any compound that is formed from carbon and hydrogen atoms only. So $C_{10}H_{22}$ (decane, an alkane) is a hydrocarbon, but $CH_3COOC_3H_7$ (an ester) is not — it's got oxygen atoms in it.

Hydrocarbons are really useful chemicals — fuels like petrol and diesel are hydrocarbons, and lots of plastics are made from hydrocarbons too.

Covalent Bonds Hold Atoms in a Molecule Together

1) All the atoms in hydrocarbon molecules are held together by covalent bonds. These covalent bonds are very strong. They form when atoms 'share' electrons.

2) This way both atoms get a full outer shell — which is an atom's main aim in life.

3) Each covalent bond provides one extra shared electron for each atom. And each atom involved has to make enough covalent bonds to fill up its outer shell. So carbon atoms always want to make a total of 4 bonds, while hydrogen atoms only want to make 1.

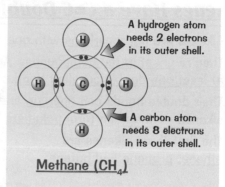

A hydrogen atom needs 2 electrons in its outer shell.

A carbon atom needs 8 electrons in its outer shell.

Methane (CH_4)

Alkanes Have All C–C Single Bonds

1) Alkanes are the simplest type of hydrocarbon you can get. They're just chains of carbon atoms with two or three hydrogen atoms attached to each one (three if the carbon's at the end of the chain, two if it's in the middle).

2) Alkanes are saturated compounds — this means they contain only single covalent bonds between their carbon atoms. (They don't have any double bonds that can open up and join onto things.)

3) You can tell the difference between an alkane and an alkene by adding the substance to bromine water — an alkane won't decolourise the bromine water (there's more about this on the next page).

4) Alkanes won't form polymers — same reason again, no double bonds to open up.

5) The first four alkanes are methane (natural gas), ethane, propane and butane.

Methane: CH_4 Ethane: C_2H_6 Propane: C_3H_8 Butane: C_4H_{10}

```
    H                 H  H              H  H  H            H  H  H  H
    |                 |  |              |  |  |            |  |  |  |
H – C – H         H – C – C – H     H – C – C – C – H   H – C – C – C – C – H
    |                 |  |              |  |  |            |  |  |  |
    H                 H  H              H  H  H            H  H  H  H
(natural gas)
```

All alkanes have the formula: C_nH_{2n+2}

The 'a' bit of these names is important because it's telling you that the molecules don't contain any double bonds. If they did, it would be an 'e' instead — like the alkenes on the next page.

Alkane anybody who doesn't learn this lot properly...

Covalent bonds are so sweet — the little atoms sharing their electrons. Heartwarming. Now warm your brain to match by learning what an alkane is — keep drawing out the structures of the examples on this page until you get the hang of the basic pattern. They're important molecules in the modern world because they make good fuels.

Hydrocarbons — Alkenes

Alkenes are another type of hydrocarbon. They're different from alkanes because they have double bonds...

Covalent Bonds can be Single or Double Bonds

1) A single covalent bond is formed when two atoms share a pair of electrons so that both can have a full outer shell (see p.19).

2) Sometimes, to fill up their outer shells, two atoms will share two pairs of electrons instead of just one pair.

3) By doing this the atoms form a double bond.

4) Carbon atoms can do this — each bond still provides one extra shared electron for each atom, but this time there are two bonds between the carbons.

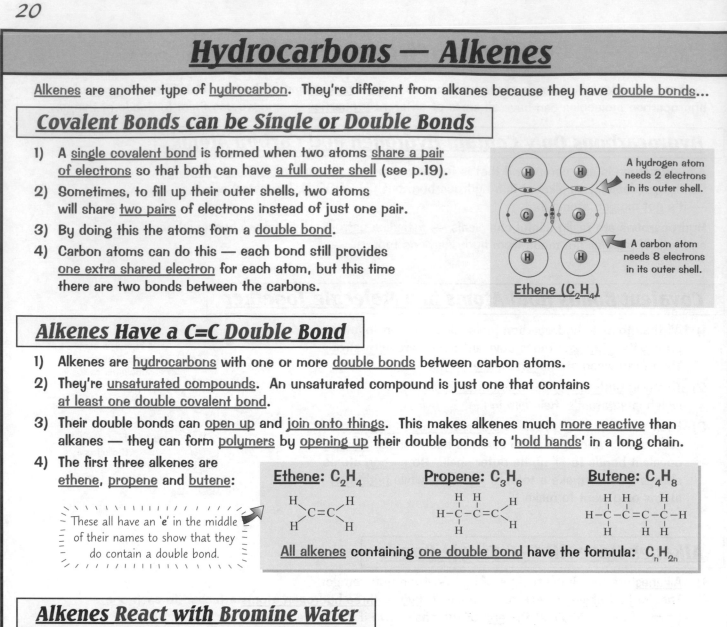

A hydrogen atom needs 2 electrons in its outer shell.

A carbon atom needs 8 electrons in its outer shell.

Ethene (C_2H_4)

Alkenes Have a C=C Double Bond

1) Alkenes are hydrocarbons with one or more double bonds between carbon atoms.

2) They're unsaturated compounds. An unsaturated compound is just one that contains at least one double covalent bond.

3) Their double bonds can open up and join onto things. This makes alkenes much more reactive than alkanes — they can form polymers by opening up their double bonds to 'hold hands' in a long chain.

4) The first three alkenes are ethene, propene and butene:

These all have an 'e' in the middle of their names to show that they do contain a double bond.

Ethene: C_2H_4

Propene: C_3H_6

Butene: C_4H_8

All alkenes containing one double bond have the formula: C_nH_{2n}

Alkenes React with Bromine Water

1) Bromine water is a bright orange solution that contains bromine (well, obviously), Br_2.

2) It's really reactive — if there are any double bonds around, they'll spring open and react with the bromine. When this happens the orange colour disappears from the solution — the bromine water is decolourised.

3) You can use this to test whether what you've got is an alkene or not. You just take a sample of your hydrocarbon, mix it with bromine water, and shake:

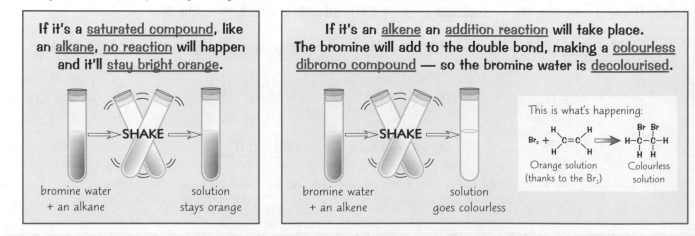

If it's a saturated compound, like an alkane, no reaction will happen and it'll stay bright orange.

SHAKE

bromine water + an alkane

solution stays orange

If it's an alkene an addition reaction will take place. The bromine will add to the double bond, making a colourless dibromo compound — so the bromine water is decolourised.

SHAKE

bromine water + an alkene

solution goes colourless

This is what's happening:

Orange solution (thanks to the Br_2)

Colourless solution

The name's bond — double covalent bond...

Just one double bond, that's all it takes, and you go from a boring, stable old alkane to a reactive alkene, forming polymers at the drop of a (metaphorical) hat and making bromine water change colour. Amazing.

Fractional Distillation of Crude Oil

Fossil fuels like coal, oil and gas are called non-renewable fuels as they take so long to make that they're being used up much faster than they're being formed. They're finite resources — one day they'll run out.

Crude Oil is Separated into Different Hydrocarbon Fractions

1) Crude oil is formed from the buried remains of plants and animals — it's a fossil fuel. Over millions of years, with high temperature and pressure, the remains turn to crude oil, which can be drilled up.

2) Crude oil is a mixture of lots of different hydrocarbons. Remember that hydrocarbons are chains of carbon atoms (e.g. alkanes and alkenes) of various lengths.

3) The different compounds in crude oil are separated by fractional distillation. The oil is heated until most of it has turned into gas. The gases enter a fractionating column (and the liquid bit, bitumen, is drained off at the bottom). In the column there's a temperature gradient (i.e. it's hot at the bottom and gets gradually cooler as you go up).

4) The longer hydrocarbons have high boiling points. They turn back into liquids and drain out of the column early on, when they're near the bottom. The shorter hydrocarbons have lower boiling points. They turn to liquid and drain out much later on, near to the top of the column where it's cooler.

5) You end up with the crude oil mixture separated out into different fractions. Each fraction contains a mixture of hydrocarbons with similar boiling points.

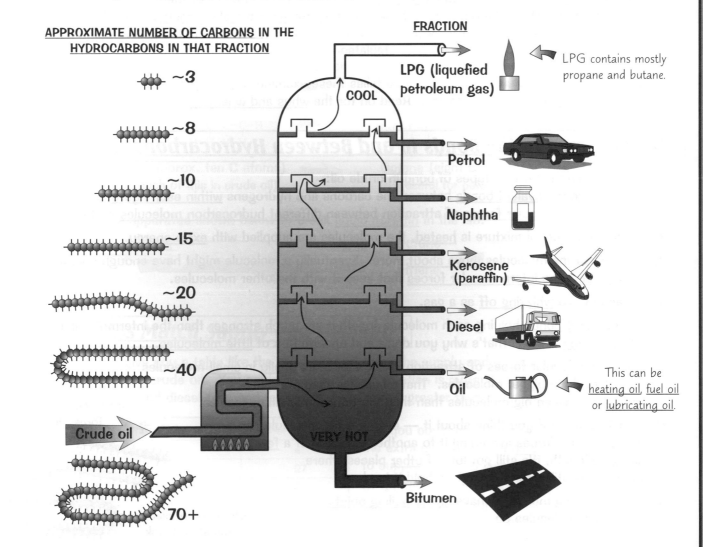

APPROXIMATE NUMBER OF CARBONS IN THE HYDROCARBONS IN THAT FRACTION

~3
~8
~10
~15
~20
~40
70+

Crude oil

VERY HOT

FRACTION

COOL

LPG (liquefied petroleum gas) — LPG contains mostly propane and butane.

Petrol

Naphtha

Kerosene (paraffin)

Diesel

Oil — This can be heating oil, fuel oil or lubricating oil.

Bitumen

How much petrol is there in crude oil? Just a fraction...

In the exam, you could be given a diagram of the fractional distillation column and asked to add labels, or say where on the column a certain fraction (like petrol or diesel) would drain off. This means you need to learn the diagram properly — don't just glance at it and assume you know it. Cover the page up and test yourself.

The Evolution of the Atmosphere

The atmosphere wasn't always like it is today. It's <u>gradually evolved</u> over billions of years and <u>we</u> have evolved with it. All very slowly. Here's one theory for how the first 4.5 billion years have gone:

Phase 1 — Volcanoes Gave Out Steam and CO₂

The First Billion Years

Steam NH₃ CO₂ CO₂ Steam NH₃

1) The Earth's surface was originally <u>molten</u> for many millions of years. Any atmosphere <u>boiled away</u>.

2) Eventually it cooled and a <u>thin crust</u> formed, but <u>volcanoes</u> kept erupting, releasing gases from <u>inside the Earth</u>. This 'degassing' released mainly <u>carbon dioxide</u>, but also <u>steam</u> and <u>ammonia</u>.

3) When things eventually settled down, the early atmosphere was <u>mostly CO₂</u> and water vapour (the water vapour later <u>condensed</u> to form the <u>oceans</u>). There was very little oxygen.

<u>Holiday report</u>: Not a nice place to be. Take strong walking boots and a good coat.

Phase 2 — Green Plants Evolved and Produced Oxygen

The Next Two Billion Years

O₂ O₂ O₂ O₂ O₂ O₂ O₂ O₂

1) A lot of the early CO₂ <u>dissolved</u> into the oceans.

2) <u>Green plants</u> evolved over most of the Earth. As they photosynthesised, they <u>removed CO₂</u> and <u>produced O₂</u>.

3) Thanks to the plants the amount of O₂ in the air gradually <u>built up</u> and much of the CO₂ eventually got <u>locked up</u> in <u>fossil fuels</u> and <u>sedimentary rocks</u> (more about this on p.33).

4) <u>Nitrogen gas (N₂)</u> was put into the atmosphere in two ways — it was formed by ammonia reacting with oxygen, and was released by denitrifying bacteria.

5) <u>N₂</u> isn't very <u>reactive</u>. So the amount of N₂ in the atmosphere <u>increased</u>, because it was being <u>made</u> but not <u>broken down</u>.

<u>Holiday Report</u>: A bit slimy underfoot. Take wellies and a lot of suncream.

Phase 3 — Ozone Layer Allows Evolution of Complex Animals

The Last Billion Years or so

Nice safe OZONE, O₃

1) The build-up of <u>oxygen</u> in the atmosphere <u>killed off</u> early organisms that couldn't tolerate it.

2) But it did allow the <u>evolution</u> of more <u>complex</u> organisms that <u>made use</u> of the oxygen.

3) The oxygen also created the <u>ozone layer (O₃)</u>, which <u>blocked</u> harmful rays from the Sun and <u>enabled</u> even <u>more complex</u> organisms to evolve.

4) There is virtually <u>no CO₂</u> left now.

<u>Holiday report</u>: A nice place to be. Get there before the crowds ruin it.

Today's Atmosphere is Just Right for Us

The <u>present composition</u> of Earth's atmosphere is:

> 78% nitrogen, 21% oxygen and 0.035% carbon dioxide
> There are also: 1) Varying amounts of <u>water vapour</u>,
>   2) And <u>noble gases</u> (mainly argon).

4 billion years ago, it was a whole other world...

It's amazing how much the atmosphere of Planet Earth has changed. The <u>climate change</u> that we're all talking about nowadays is small beer in comparison (though it's massively important to <u>us</u> of course).

The Carbon Cycle

There's a scientific consensus that <u>human activities</u> are <u>changing</u> the proportion of <u>carbon dioxide</u> in the <u>atmosphere</u> — and that that's going to have <u>massive effects</u> on life on Earth. You need to understand the <u>science</u> behind the scary headlines, and to do that you first need to understand the <u>carbon cycle</u>.

Carbon is Constantly Being Recycled

Carbon is the key to the greenhouse effect — it exists in the atmosphere as carbon dioxide gas, and is also present in many other <u>greenhouse gases</u> (e.g. methane).

1) The carbon on Earth moves in a big cycle — the diagram below is a pretty good summary.

2) <u>Respiration</u>, <u>combustion</u> and <u>decay</u> of plants and animals add carbon dioxide to the air and remove oxygen.

3) <u>Photosynthesis</u> does the <u>opposite</u> — it removes carbon dioxide and adds oxygen.

4) These processes should all <u>balance out</u>. However, <u>humans</u> have upset the natural carbon cycle, which has affected the balance of gases in the atmosphere.

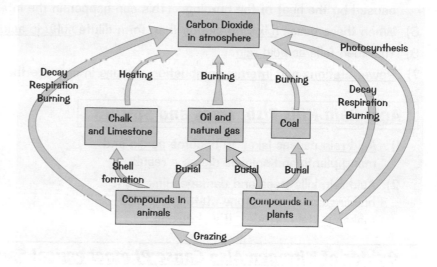

Human Activity Affects the Composition of Air

1) The <u>human population is increasing</u>. This means there are more people <u>respiring</u> — giving out <u>more carbon dioxide</u>. But that's not the half of it...

2) More people means that <u>more energy</u> is needed for lighting, heating, cooking, transport and so on. And people's <u>lifestyles</u> are changing too. More and more countries are becoming <u>industrialised</u> and <u>well-off</u>. This means the average <u>energy demand per person</u> is also increasing (since people have <u>more electrical gadgets</u> at home, more people have <u>cars</u>, and more people <u>travel on planes</u>, etc.).

This increased energy consumption comes mainly from the <u>burning of fossil fuels</u>, which releases <u>more carbon dioxide</u>.

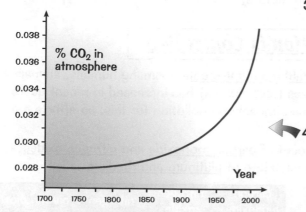

3) More people also means more land is needed to build <u>houses</u> and grow <u>food</u>. This space is often made by <u>chopping down trees</u> — this is called <u>deforestation</u>. But plants are the main things <u>taking carbon dioxide out of the atmosphere</u> (as they photosynthesise) — so fewer plants means less carbon dioxide is <u>taken out</u> of the atmosphere.

4) The graph shows how CO_2 levels in the atmosphere have risen over the last 150 years.

Eeeek — the carbon cycle's got a puncture...

For <u>each person</u> on a <u>one-way</u> flight from London to New York, a whopping 600 kg of carbon dioxide is added to the air. If you feel bad about the amount of carbon dioxide that flying off on your holidays releases, you can <u>balance</u> it by paying for <u>trees</u> to be planted. There are companies that'll tell you just how many trees need to be planted to balance the carbon dioxide released by your flight.

Air Pollution and Acid Rain

Increasing carbon dioxide is causing climate change. But CO_2 isn't the only gas released when fossil fuels burn — you also get other nasties like oxides of nitrogen, sulfur dioxide and carbon monoxide.

Acid Rain is Caused by Sulfur Dioxide and Oxides of Nitrogen

1) When fossil fuels are burned they release mostly CO_2 (a big cause of global warming).
2) But they also release other harmful gases — especially sulfur dioxide and various nitrogen oxides.
3) The sulfur dioxide (SO_2) comes from sulfur impurities in the fossil fuels.
4) However, the nitrogen oxides are created from a reaction between the nitrogen and oxygen in the air, caused by the heat of the burning. (This can happen in the internal combustion engines of cars.)
5) When these gases mix with clouds they form dilute sulfuric acid and dilute nitric acid.
6) This then falls as acid rain.
7) Power stations and internal combustion engines in cars are the main causes of acid rain.

Acid Rain Kills Fish, Trees and Statues

1) Acid rain causes lakes to become acidic and many plants and animals die as a result.
2) Acid rain kills trees and damages limestone buildings and ruins stone statues. It also makes metal corrode. It's shocking.

Oxides of Nitrogen Also Cause Photochemical Smog

Photochemical smog is a type of air pollution caused by sunlight acting on oxides of nitrogen.
These oxides combine with oxygen in the air to produce ozone (O_3).
Ozone can cause breathing difficulties, headaches and tiredness.
(Don't confuse ground-level ozone with the useful ozone layer high up in the atmosphere.)

Carbon Monoxide is a Poisonous Gas

1) Carbon monoxide (CO) can stop your blood doing its proper job of carrying oxygen around the body.
2) A lack of oxygen in the blood can lead to fainting, a coma or even death.
3) Carbon monoxide is formed when petrol or diesel in car engines is burnt without enough oxygen — this is incomplete combustion (see page 25 for more details).

It's Important That Atmospheric Pollution is Controlled

1) The build-up of all these pollutants can make life unhealthy and miserable for many humans, animals and plants. The number of cases of respiratory illnesses (e.g. asthma) has increased in recent years — especially among young people. Many people blame atmospheric pollution for this, so efforts are being made to improve things.
2) Catalytic converters on motor vehicles reduce the amount of carbon monoxide and nitrogen oxides getting into the atmosphere. The catalyst is normally a mixture of platinum and rhodium.

It helps unpleasant exhaust gases from the car react to make things that are less immediately dangerous (though more CO_2 is still not exactly ideal).

carbon monoxide	+	nitrogen oxide	→ nitrogen	+	carbon dioxide
$2CO$	+	$2NO$	$\rightarrow$ N_2	+	$2CO_2$

Revision and pollution — the two bugbears of modern life...

Eeee.... cars and fossil fuels — they're nowt but trouble. But at least this topic is kind of interesting, what with its relevance to everyday life and all. Just think... you could see this kind of stuff on TV.

Revision Summary for Module C1

Okay, if you were just about to turn the page without doing these revision summary questions, then stop. What kind of an attitude is that... Is that really the way you want to live your life... running, playing and having fun... Of course not. That's right. Do the questions. It's for the best all round.

1)* A molecule has the molecular formula $CH_3(CH_2)_4CH_3$. How many H and C atoms does it contain?
2)* Write down the displayed formula for a molecule with the molecular formula C_3H_8.
3) Write down the symbol equation for magnesium reacting with oxygen.
4)* Balance this equation which shows sodium reacting with water: $Na + H_2O \rightarrow NaOH + H_2$.
5) Define the word 'hydrophobic'.
6) What is an emulsifier? Briefly explain how an emulsifier does its job.
7) Explain why we don't eat uncooked potatoes.
8) Give the word equation for the thermal decomposition of baking powder (sodium hydrogencarbonate).
9) Esterification produces an ester and water — what are the reactants?
10) Give three properties that a substance must have in order to make a good perfume.
11) A substance keeps the same volume, but changes its shape according to the container it's held in. Is it a solid, a liquid or a gas? How strong are the forces of attraction between its particles?
12) What does it mean if a liquid is said to be very volatile?
13) In salt water, what is: a) the solute, b) the solution?
14) Explain why nail varnish doesn't dissolve in water.
15) Paint is a colloid — what is a colloid?
16) How does oil paint dry?
17) What are thermochromic pigments? Give four uses for them.
18) What makes glow-in-the-dark watches glow in the dark?
19) Name the monomer that's used to make polythene.
20) Plastic bags stretch and melt easily. Are the forces between the polymer chains weak or strong?
21) Give one disadvantage of burning plastics and one disadvantage of burying them.
22) Give the general formula for an alkene containing one double bond.
23) Describe a test you can do to tell whether a particular hydrocarbon is an alkene.
24) True or false: in a fractionating column the shortest hydrocarbons leave the column at the bottom.
25) Give three ways that the properties of hydrocarbons change as they increase in size.
26) Why can small hydrocarbon molecules change state from liquid to gas more easily than big ones?
27) What is cracking used for?
28) What two conditions are needed for cracking to happen, and why?
29) Explain why the amount of fossil fuels being used is increasing all the time.
30) Explain why having few oil and gas reserves might become a problem for a country like the UK.
31) How might an oil slick harm sea birds?
32) Give four factors which affect the choice of fuel for a job.
33) Give two advantages of complete combustion over incomplete combustion.
34)* Write down a balanced symbol equation for the incomplete combustion of ethane (C_2H_6).
35) 3 billion years ago, the Earth's atmosphere was mostly CO_2. Where did this CO_2 come from?
36) Today, there's mostly O_2 and N_2 in the Earth's atmosphere. What process produced the O_2? What two processes produced the N_2?
37) Sketch and label a diagram of the carbon cycle.
38) What kind of air pollution makes limestone buildings and statues look worn?
39) Name a poisonous gas that catalytic converters help to remove from car exhausts.

* Answers on page 108.

The Earth's Structure

This page is all about the <u>structure</u> of <u>the Earth</u> — what the planet's like inside, and how scientists study it...

The Earth has a Crust, a Mantle and a Core

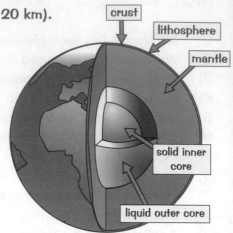

1) The <u>crust</u> is Earth's thin outer layer of solid rock (its average depth is 20 km).

2) The <u>lithosphere</u> includes the crust and upper part of the <u>mantle</u>, and is made up of a <u>jigsaw</u> of 'tectonic plates'. The <u>lithosphere</u> is <u>relatively cold and rigid</u>, and is over 100 km thick in places.

3) The <u>mantle</u> is the <u>solid</u> section between the crust and the core. Near the crust it's <u>very rigid</u>. As you go deeper into the mantle the <u>temperature increases</u> — here it becomes <u>less rigid</u> and can <u>flow very slowly</u> (it behaves like it's semi-liquid).

4) The <u>core</u> is just over <u>half</u> the Earth's radius. The <u>inner core</u> is <u>solid</u>, while the <u>outer core</u> is <u>liquid</u>.

5) <u>Radioactive decay</u> creates a lot of the <u>heat</u> inside the Earth. This heat creates <u>convection currents</u> in the mantle, which causes the <u>plates</u> of the lithosphere to <u>move</u>.

The Earth's Surface is Made Up of Large Plates of Rock

1) <u>Tectonic plates</u> are like <u>big rocky rafts</u> that <u>float</u> on the mantle (they're <u>less dense</u> than the mantle).

2) This map shows where the <u>edges</u> of the plates are. As they <u>move</u>, the <u>continents</u> move too.

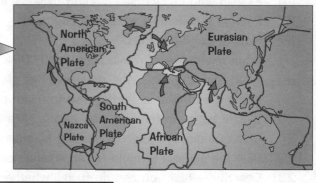

3) The plates move very slowly — at a speed of about <u>2.5 cm per year</u>.

4) <u>Volcanoes</u> and <u>earthquakes</u> often occur where the plates meet. It's the <u>movement</u> of the plates against each other that causes them.

Seismic Waves Can Tell Us What's Below The Crust

1) It's difficult to study the <u>inner structure</u> of the Earth — you can't get at it directly, because the crust is <u>too thick</u> to drill through.

2) Scientists use <u>seismic waves</u> (shock waves) to study the Earth's structure. These are produced by <u>earthquakes</u>. Seismic waves can also be produced by setting off a big <u>man-made explosion</u> at the Earth's surface.

3) By measuring the <u>time</u> that it takes for these waves to travel through the Earth, and <u>where</u> they are detected, scientists can draw conclusions about the <u>structure</u> of the Earth.

There are <u>two types</u> of seismic wave that can travel through the Earth — <u>P-waves</u> and <u>S-waves</u>. P-waves travel through solids and liquids. S-waves can only travel through solids.

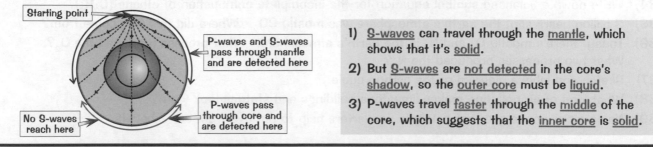

1) <u>S-waves</u> can travel through the <u>mantle</u>, which shows that it's <u>solid</u>.

2) But <u>S-waves</u> are <u>not detected</u> in the core's <u>shadow</u>, so the <u>outer core</u> must be <u>liquid</u>.

3) P-waves travel <u>faster</u> through the <u>middle</u> of the core, which suggests that the <u>inner core</u> is <u>solid</u>.

2.5 cm a year — that's as fast as your fingernails grow...

So everyone standing on the surface of our little blue-green planet is actually <u>floating</u> round very slowly on a sea of <u>semi-liquid rock</u>. Make sure you understand the stuff about <u>tectonic plates</u> — there's more coming up...

Plate Tectonics

The idea that the Earth's surface is made up of <u>moving plates of rock</u> has been around since the early twentieth century. But it took a while to <u>catch on</u>.

Observations About the Earth Hadn't Been Explained

1) For years, fossils of <u>very similar</u> plants and animals had been found on <u>opposite sides</u> of the Atlantic Ocean. Most people thought this was because the continents had been <u>linked</u> by '<u>land bridges</u>', which had <u>sunk</u> or been <u>covered</u> by water as the Earth <u>cooled</u>. But not everyone was convinced, even back then.

2) Other things about the Earth puzzled people too — like why the <u>coastlines</u> of <u>Africa</u> and <u>South America</u> fit together and why there are fossils of <u>sea creatures</u> in the <u>Alps</u>.

Identical fossils of the same freshwater crocodile found in both South America and South Africa

Explaining These Observations Needed a Leap of Imagination

What was needed was a scientist with a bit of <u>insight</u>... a smidgeon of <u>creativity</u>... a touch of <u>genius</u>...

1) In 1914 <u>Alfred Wegener</u> hypothesised that Africa and South America had previously been <u>one</u> continent which had then <u>split</u>. He started to look for more evidence to <u>back up</u> his hypothesis. He found it...

2) E.g. there were <u>matching layers</u> in the <u>rocks</u> on different continents, and similar <u>earthworms</u> living in <u>both</u> South America and South Africa.

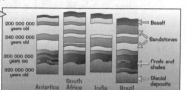

3) Wegener's theory of '<u>continental drift</u>' supposed that about 300 million years ago there had been just one '<u>supercontinent</u>' — which he called Pangaea. According to Wegener, Pangaea broke into smaller chunks, and these chunks (our modern-day <u>continents</u>) are still slowly 'drifting' apart. This idea is the basis behind the modern theory of <u>plate tectonics</u>.

The Theory Wasn't Accepted at First — for a Variety of Reasons

1) Wegener's theory <u>explained</u> things that <u>couldn't</u> be explained by the 'land bridge' theory (e.g. the formation of <u>mountains</u> — which Wegener said happened as continents <u>smashed into</u> each other). But it was a big change, and the reaction from other scientists was <u>hostile</u>.

2) The main problem was that Wegener's explanation of <u>how</u> the '<u>drifting</u>' happened wasn't convincing (and the movement wasn't <u>detectable</u>). Wegener claimed the continents' movement could be caused by tidal forces and the Earth's rotation — but other geologists showed that this was <u>impossible</u>.

Eventually, the Evidence Became Overwhelming

1) In the 1960s, scientists investigated the <u>Mid-Atlantic ridge</u>, which runs the <u>whole length</u> of the Atlantic.

2) They found evidence that <u>magma</u> (molten rock) <u>rises up</u> through the sea floor, <u>solidifies</u> and forms underwater mountains that are <u>roughly symmetrical</u> either side of the ridge. The evidence suggested that the sea floor was <u>spreading</u> — at about 10 cm per year.

3) Even better evidence that the continents are moving apart came from the <u>magnetic orientation</u> of the rocks. As the liquid magma erupts out of the gap, <u>iron particles</u> in the rocks tend to <u>align themselves</u> with the Earth's <u>magnetic field</u> — and as it cools they <u>set</u> in position. Now then... every half million years or so the Earth's magnetic field <u>swaps direction</u> — and the rock on <u>either side</u> of the ridge has <u>bands</u> of <u>alternate magnetic polarity</u>, <u>symmetrical</u> about the ridge.

4) This was convincing evidence that new sea floor was being created... and <u>continents</u> were <u>moving apart</u>.

5) All the evidence collected by other scientists <u>supported Wegener's theory</u> — so it was gradually <u>accepted</u>.

I told you so — but no one ever believes me...

Wegener wasn't right about everything, but his <u>main idea</u> was <u>correct</u>. The scientific community was a bit slow to accept it, but once there was more <u>evidence</u> to support it, they got on board. That's science for you...

Volcanic Eruptions

The theory of <u>plate tectonics</u> not only explains why the continents move, it also makes sense of natural hazards such as <u>volcanoes</u> and <u>earthquakes</u>.

Volcanoes are Formed by Molten Rock

1) Volcanoes occur when <u>molten rock</u> (<u>magma</u>) from the <u>mantle</u> emerges through the Earth's crust.

2) Magma rises up (through the crust) and 'boils over' where it can — sometimes quite violently if the pressure is released suddenly. (When the molten rock is <u>below</u> the surface of the Earth it's called <u>magma</u> — but when it <u>erupts</u> from a volcano it's called <u>lava</u>.)

Oceanic and Continental Crust Colliding Causes Volcanoes

1) The crust at the <u>ocean floor</u> is <u>denser</u> than the crust below the <u>continents</u>.

2) When two tectonic plates collide, a dense <u>oceanic plate</u> will be <u>forced underneath</u> a less dense <u>continental plate</u>. This is called <u>subduction</u>.

3) Oceanic crust also tends to be <u>cooler</u> at the <u>edges</u> of a tectonic plate — so the edges <u>sink</u> easily, <u>pulling</u> the oceanic plate <u>down</u>.

4) As the oceanic crust is forced down it <u>melts</u> and <u>starts to rise</u>. If this <u>molten rock</u> finds its way to the <u>surface</u>, <u>volcanoes</u> form.

Diagram labels: Volcano, Fold mountains, Oceanic trench, Oceanic crust, Continental crust, Magma, Melting

Volcanic Activity Forms Igneous Rock

1) <u>Igneous rock</u> is made when any sort of <u>molten rock cools down</u> and <u>solidifies</u>. Lots of rocks on the surface of the Earth were formed this way.

2) The <u>type</u> of igneous rock (and the behaviour of the volcano) depends on how <u>quickly</u> the magma <u>cools</u> and the <u>composition of the magma</u>.

3) Some volcanoes produce magma that forms <u>iron-rich basalt</u>. The lava from the eruption is runny, and the eruption is <u>fairly safe</u>. (As safe as you can be with molten rock at 1200 °C, I suppose.)

4) But if the magma is <u>silica-rich rhyolite</u>, the eruption is <u>explosive</u>. It produces <u>thick lava</u> which can be violently blown out of the top of the volcano. Crikey.

Geologists Try to Predict Volcanic Eruptions

1) Geologists study volcanoes to try to find out if there are <u>signs</u> that a volcanic eruption might happen soon — things like <u>magma movement</u> below the ground near to a volcano.

2) Being able to spot these kinds of clues means that scientists can <u>predict eruptions</u> with much <u>greater accuracy</u> than they could in the past.

3) It's tricky though — volcanoes are very unpredictable. Most likely, scientists will only be able to say that an eruption's <u>more likely than normal</u> — not that it's <u>certain</u>. But even just knowing that can <u>save lives</u>.

Make the Earth move for you — stand next to a volcano...

Volcanoes can erupt with huge force, so it might seem odd to choose to <u>live</u> near one. But there are <u>benefits</u> — volcanic ash creates very <u>fertile soil</u> that's great for farming. It would be much <u>safer</u> if eruptions could be <u>predicted</u> accurately — geologists aren't there yet, but their predictions are getting better all the time.

The Three Different Types of Rock

Scientists classify rocks according to how they're formed. The three different types are: <u>sedimentary</u>, <u>metamorphic</u> and <u>igneous</u>. Sedimentary rocks are generally pretty soft, while igneous rocks are well hard.

There are Three Steps in the Formation of Sedimentary Rock

1) <u>Sedimentary rocks</u> are formed from <u>layers of sediment</u> laid down in <u>lakes</u> or <u>seas</u>.

2) Over <u>millions of years</u> the layers get <u>buried</u> under more layers and the <u>weight</u> pressing down <u>squeezes out</u> the water.

3) Fluids flowing through the pores deposit natural mineral <u>cement</u>.

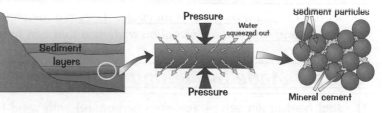

Limestone is a Sedimentary Rock Formed from Seashells

1) Limestone is mostly formed from <u>seashells</u>. It's mostly <u>calcium carbonate</u> and <u>grey/white</u> in colour. The original <u>shells</u> are mostly <u>crushed</u>, but there can still be quite a few <u>fossilised shells</u> remaining.

2) When limestone is heated it <u>thermally decomposes</u> to make <u>calcium oxide</u> and <u>carbon dioxide</u>:

calcium carbonate → calcium oxide + carbon dioxide
$CaCO_3(s)$ → $CaO(s)$ + $CO_2(g)$

Thermal decomposition is when one substance <u>chemically breaks down</u> into at least two <u>new substances</u> when it's <u>heated</u>.

Metamorphic Rocks are Formed from Other Rocks

1) <u>Metamorphic rocks</u> are formed by the action of <u>heat and pressure</u> on <u>sedimentary</u> (or even <u>igneous</u>) <u>rocks</u> over <u>long periods</u> of time.

2) The <u>mineral structure</u> and <u>texture</u> may be different, but the chemical composition is often the same.

3) So long as the rocks don't actually <u>melt</u> they're classed as <u>metamorphic</u>. If they <u>melt</u> and turn to <u>magma</u>, they're <u>gone</u> (though they may eventually resurface as igneous rocks).

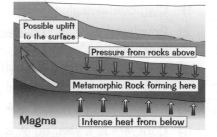

Marble is a Metamorphic Rock Formed from Limestone

1) Marble is another form of <u>calcium carbonate</u>.

2) Very high temperatures and pressures <u>break down</u> the limestone and it reforms as <u>small crystals</u>.

3) This gives marble a <u>more even texture</u> and makes it <u>much harder</u>.

Igneous Rocks are Formed from Fresh Magma

1) <u>Igneous rocks</u> are formed when <u>magma</u> cools (see previous page).

2) They contain various <u>different minerals</u> in <u>randomly arranged</u> interlocking <u>crystals</u> — this makes them very <u>hard</u>.

3) Granite is a <u>very hard</u> igneous rock (even harder than marble). It's ideal for <u>steps</u> and <u>buildings</u>.

Igneous rocks are real cool — or they're magma...

There are a few scientific terms on this page that you need to learn, but there's nothing too tricky to get your head round. Just remember that <u>limestone</u> is a <u>sedimentary rock</u>, <u>marble</u> is a <u>metamorphic rock</u> and <u>granite</u> is an <u>igneous rock</u>. And that's why granite is harder than marble, which is harder than limestone. Job's a good 'un.

Construction Materials

Loads of different construction materials are made from stuff found in the Earth's crust.
For example, there are metals like aluminium and iron, rocks such as granite, limestone and marble,
and then there are man-made materials like bricks, cement, concrete and glass.

Aluminium and Iron are Extracted from Ores in Rocks

Rocks are usually a mixture of minerals. Ores are minerals we can get useful materials from.
Aluminium and iron are construction materials that can be extracted from their ores.

Glass is Made by Melting Limestone, Sand and Soda

1) Just heat up limestone (calcium carbonate) with sand (silicon dioxide)
   and soda (sodium carbonate) until it melts.

2) When the mixture cools it comes out as glass.
   It's as easy as that. Eat your heart out Mr Pilkington.

Bricks are Made from Clay

1) Clay is a mineral formed from weathered and decomposed rock. It's soft
   when it's dug up out of the ground, which makes it easy to mould into bricks.

2) But it can be hardened by firing at very high temperatures. This makes it ideal as a
   building material — bricks can withstand the weight of lots more bricks on top of them.

Limestone and Clay are Heated to Make Cement

1) Clay contains aluminium and silicates.

2) Powdered clay and powdered limestone are roasted in a rotating kiln to
   make a complex mixture of calcium and aluminium silicates, called cement.

3) When cement is mixed with water a slow chemical reaction takes place.
   This causes the cement to gradually set hard.

4) Cement can be mixed with sand, aggregate (gravelly stuff) and water to make concrete.

5) Concrete is a very quick and cheap way of constructing buildings — and it shows...
   — concrete has got to be the most hideously unattractive building material ever known.

6) Reinforced concrete is a 'composite material' — it's a combination of concrete and a solid steel support
   (like steel rods). It's a better construction material than ordinary concrete because it combines the
   hardness of concrete with the flexibility and the strength of steel. (It isn't any prettier than plain old concrete though...)

Extracting Rocks Can Cause Environmental Damage

1) Quarrying uses up land and destroys habitats. It costs money to make quarry sites look pretty again.

2) Transporting rock can cause noise and pollution.

3) The quarrying process itself produces dust and makes a lot of noise
   — they often use dynamite to blast the rock out of the ground.

4) Disused sites can be dangerous. Every year people drown in former quarries that have been
   turned into (very very deep) lakes. Disused mines have been known to collapse — this can cause
   subsidence (including huge holes appearing and buildings cracking, railway lines twisting etc.).

Bricks are like eggs — they both have to be laid...

If red houses are made of red bricks and blue houses are made of blue bricks, then what colour bricks are
greenhouses made of? If you said green, then you're not properly awake and most likely you need to go back
and read the page again. If you correctly identified that a greenhouse is made of glass rather than green bricks,
then continue to the next page. Once you've learnt all the above, obviously.

Extracting Pure Copper

Copper is dug out of the ground as a copper ore (like chalcopyrite or malachite). Then the metal is extracted from it by mixing the ore with carbon and heating. The copper you get this way isn't pure enough to use in electrical conductors (the purer it is, the better it conducts). But it can be purified using another method...

Electrolysis is Used to Obtain Very Pure Copper

1) Electrolysis means "splitting up with electricity" — in this case passing a current through a piece of impure copper splits the pure copper off from the nasty impurities.

2) The copper is immersed in a liquid (called the electrolyte) which conducts electricity. Electrolytes are usually free ions dissolved in water. Copper(II) sulfate solution is the electrolyte used in purifying copper — it contains Cu^{2+} ions.

3) The electrical supply acts like an electron pump. This is what happens:

> 1) It pulls electrons off copper atoms at the anode, causing them to go into solution as Cu^{2+} ions.
> 2) It then offers electrons at the cathode to nearby Cu^{2+} ions to turn them back into copper atoms.
> 3) The impurities are dropped at the anode as a sludge, whilst pure copper atoms bond to the cathode.

Here's a diagram of the apparatus you need for the job — you could be asked to label it in the exam, so make sure you learn it.

The cathode is the negative electrode. It starts as a thin piece of pure copper and more pure copper adds to it.

Pure copper is deposited on the pure cathode (–ve)

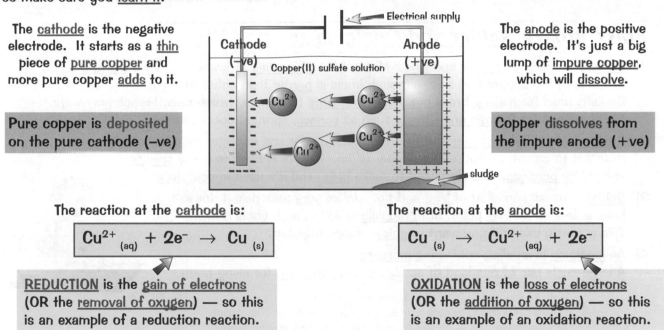

The anode is the positive electrode. It's just a big lump of impure copper, which will dissolve.

Copper dissolves from the impure anode (+ve)

The reaction at the cathode is:

$$Cu^{2+}_{(aq)} + 2e^- \rightarrow Cu_{(s)}$$

REDUCTION is the gain of electrons (OR the removal of oxygen) — so this is an example of a reduction reaction.

The reaction at the anode is:

$$Cu_{(s)} \rightarrow Cu^{2+}_{(aq)} + 2e^-$$

OXIDATION is the loss of electrons (OR the addition of oxygen) — so this is an example of an oxidation reaction.

During electrolysis, copper dissolves away from the anode and is deposited at the cathode. So the anode loses mass and the cathode gains mass. (The electrolysis process is often allowed to go on for weeks and the cathode can be twenty times bigger at the end of it.)

Recycling Copper Saves Money and Resources

1) It's cheaper to recycle copper than it is to mine and extract new copper from its ore.

2) And recycling copper uses only 15% of the energy that'd be used to mine and extract the same amount.

3) But it can be hard to convince people that it's worth the effort to sort and recycle their metal waste. Even then you have to sort out the copper from all the other waste metal — which takes time and energy.

Revision and electrolysis — they can both go on for weeks...

Don't get tripped up by the two definitions of oxidation/reduction on this page. You need to know both of them — but it's important to remember that in this case you aren't adding or removing any oxygen, just electrons. Make sure you've got a handle on how electrolysis works — it's a really useful way to purify metals...

Alloys

Different metals have different properties, but by combining them with other elements you can create a new material that keeps some of the properties of the original materials, and has some extra properties too.

An Alloy is a Mixture of a Metal and Other Elements

1) Alloys can be a mixture of two or more different metals (like brass or bronze).

2) They can also be a mixture of a metal and a non-metal (like steel).

3) Alloys often have properties that are different from the metals they are made from
— and these new properties often make the alloy more useful than the pure metal.

Steel is an Alloy of Iron and Carbon

1) Steel is harder than iron.

2) Steel is also stronger than iron, as long as the amount of carbon does not get larger than about 1%.

3) Iron on its own will rust (corrode) fairly quickly, but steel is much less likely to rust.
A small amount of carbon makes a big difference.

4) A lot of things are made from steel — girders, bridges, engine parts, cutlery, washing machines, saucepans, ships, drill bits, cars etc. There's more about steel in car manufacture on the next page.

Brass, Bronze, Solder and Amalgam are also Alloys

1) Brass is an alloy of copper and zinc. Most of the properties of brass are just a mixture of those of the copper and zinc, although brass is harder than either of them.
Brass is used for making brass musical instruments (trumpets, trombones, French horns etc.).
It's also used for fixtures and fittings such as screws, springs, doorknobs etc.

2) Bronze is an alloy of copper and tin. It's much harder and stronger than tin, and it's more resistant to corrosion than either copper or tin. Bronze is used to make springs and motor bearings. It's also used to make bells, and it's used in sculpture.

3) Solder is usually an alloy of lead and tin. Unlike pure materials it doesn't have a definite melting point, but gradually solidifies as it cools down.
This is pretty useful if you want to solder things together.

4) An amalgam is an alloy containing mercury.
A large-scale use of one kind of amalgam is in dentistry, for filling teeth.

> Modern fillings tend to be made from tooth-coloured resin instead. This is partly because amalgam fillings are dark silvery in colour, and therefore rather obvious in your mouth, and partly because some people worry that the mercury in the amalgam could cause health problems (although there's not much evidence for this).

Some Alloys are Smart

1) Nitinol is the name given to a family of alloys of nickel and titanium that have shape memory.

2) This means they "remember" their original shape, and go back to it even after being bent and twisted.

3) This has increased the number of uses for alloys. You can get specs with Nitinol frames
— these can be bent and even sat on and they still go back into their original shape.

I eat bits of metal all day — it's my staple diet...

You need metals or alloys with different properties for different uses. For example, to make an engine part that's going to get very hot, you need to use something with a high melting point. And if you're building an aircraft you're going to need something that's strong and light. If you get a question in the exam about what alloy is best for a particular job, just use a bit of common sense and you'll be fine.

Building Cars

There are loads of different materials in your average car — different materials have different properties and so have different uses. Makes sense.

Iron and Steel Corrode Much More than Aluminium

Iron corrodes easily. In other words, it rusts. ◄── The word "rust" is only used for the corrosion of iron, not other metals.

Rusting only happens when the iron's in contact with both oxygen (from the air) and water.

The chemical reaction that takes place when iron corrodes is an oxidation reaction. The iron gains oxygen to form iron(III) oxide. Water then becomes loosely bonded to the iron(III) oxide and the result is hydrated iron(III) oxide — which we call rust.

Learn the word equation for the reaction:

| iron + oxygen + water → hydrated iron(III) oxide |

Unfortunately, rust is a soft crumbly solid that soon flakes off to leave more iron available to rust again. And if the water's salty or acidic, rusting will take place a lot quicker. Cars in coastal places rust a lot because they get covered in salty sea-spray. Cars in dry deserty places hardly rust at all.

Aluminium doesn't corrode when it's wet. This is a bit odd because aluminium is more reactive than iron. What happens is that the aluminium reacts very quickly with oxygen in the air to form aluminium oxide. A nice protective layer of aluminium oxide sticks firmly to the aluminium below and stops any further reaction taking place (the oxide isn't crumbly and flaky like rust, so it won't fall off).

Car Bodies: Aluminium or Steel?

Aluminium has two big advantages over steel:

1) It has a much lower density, so the car body of an aluminium car will be lighter than the same car made of steel. This gives the aluminium car much better fuel economy, which saves fuel resources.

2) A car body made with aluminium corrodes less and so it'll have a longer lifetime.

But aluminium has a massive disadvantage. It costs a lot more than iron or steel. That's why car manufacturers tend to build cars out of steel instead.

You Need Various Materials to Build Different Bits of a Car

1) Steel is strong and it can be hammered into sheets and welded together — good for the bodywork.

2) Aluminium is strong and has a low density — it's used for parts of the engine, to reduce weight.

3) Glass is transparent — cars need windscreens and windows.

4) Plastics are light and hardwearing, so they're used as internal coverings for doors, dashboards etc. They're also electrical insulators, used for covering electrical wires.

5) Fibres (natural and synthetic) are hard-wearing, so they're used to cover the seats and floor.

Unless you can afford leather seats, that is.

Recycling Cars is Important

1) As with all recycling, the idea is to save natural resources, save money and reduce landfill use.

2) At the moment a lot of the metal from a scrap car is recycled, though most of the other materials (e.g. plastics, rubber etc.) go into landfill. But European laws are now in place saying that 85% of the materials in a car (rising to 95% of a car by 2015) must be recyclable.

3) The biggest problem with recycling all the non-metal bits of a car is that they have to be separated before they can be recycled. Sorting out different types of plastic is a pain in the neck.

CGP jokes — 85% recycled since 1996...

When manufacturers choose materials for cars, they have to weigh up alternatives — they balance safety, environmental impact, and cost. In the exam, you could be asked to do the same. Sounds fun.

Acids and Bases

You'll find acids and bases <u>at home</u>, in <u>industry</u> and in <u>the lab</u> — they're an important set of chemicals.

The pH Scale and Universal Indicator

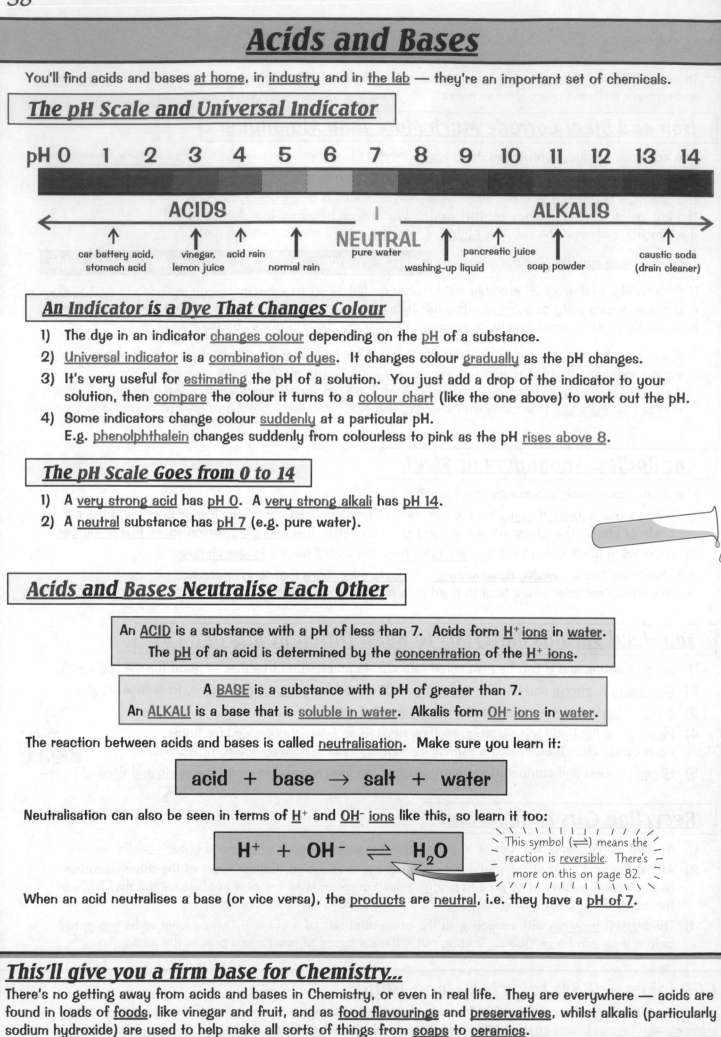

pH 0 1 2 3 4 5 6 7 8 9 10 11 12 13 14

ACIDS | ALKALIS
                    NEUTRAL

car battery acid,   vinegar,   acid rain   pure water   pancreatic juice   caustic soda
stomach acid   lemon juice   soap powder   (drain cleaner)
                              normal rain   washing-up liquid

An Indicator is a Dye That Changes Colour

1) The dye in an indicator <u>changes colour</u> depending on the <u>pH</u> of a substance.

2) <u>Universal indicator</u> is a <u>combination of dyes</u>. It changes colour <u>gradually</u> as the pH changes.

3) It's very useful for <u>estimating</u> the pH of a solution. You just add a drop of the indicator to your solution, then <u>compare</u> the colour it turns to a <u>colour chart</u> (like the one above) to work out the pH.

4) Some indicators change colour <u>suddenly</u> at a particular pH.
   E.g. <u>phenolphthalein</u> changes suddenly from colourless to pink as the pH <u>rises above 8</u>.

The pH Scale Goes from 0 to 14

1) A <u>very strong acid</u> has <u>pH 0</u>. A <u>very strong alkali</u> has <u>pH 14</u>.

2) A <u>neutral</u> substance has <u>pH 7</u> (e.g. pure water).

Acids and Bases Neutralise Each Other

An <u>ACID</u> is a substance with a pH of less than 7. Acids form H^+ ions in <u>water</u>.
The <u>pH</u> of an acid is determined by the <u>concentration</u> of the H^+ ions.

A <u>BASE</u> is a substance with a pH of greater than 7.
An <u>ALKALI</u> is a base that is <u>soluble in water</u>. Alkalis form OH^- ions in <u>water</u>.

The reaction between acids and bases is called <u>neutralisation</u>. Make sure you learn it:

$$acid \; + \; base \; \rightarrow \; salt \; + \; water$$

Neutralisation can also be seen in terms of $\underline{H^+}$ and $\underline{OH^-}$ <u>ions</u> like this, so learn it too:

$$H^+ \; + \; OH^- \; \rightleftharpoons \; H_2O$$

This symbol ($\rightleftharpoons$) means the reaction is <u>reversible</u>. There's more on this on page 82.

When an acid neutralises a base (or vice versa), the <u>products</u> are <u>neutral</u>, i.e. they have a <u>pH of 7</u>.

This'll give you a firm base for Chemistry...

There's no getting away from acids and bases in Chemistry, or even in real life. They are everywhere — acids are found in loads of <u>foods</u>, like vinegar and fruit, and as <u>food flavourings</u> and <u>preservatives</u>, whilst alkalis (particularly sodium hydroxide) are used to help make all sorts of things from <u>soaps</u> to <u>ceramics</u>.

Reactions of Acids

When you mix an <u>acid</u> and a <u>base</u>, exactly what you end up with depends on which acid and base you use...

Metal Oxides and Metal Hydroxides are Bases

1) Some <u>metal oxides</u> and <u>metal hydroxides</u> dissolve in <u>water</u>. These soluble compounds are <u>alkalis</u>.

2) Even <u>bases</u> that won't <u>dissolve</u> in water will still react with acids.

3) So, all <u>metal oxides</u> and <u>metal hydroxides</u> react with <u>acids</u> to form a <u>salt</u> and <u>water</u>.

> Acid + Metal Oxide → Salt + Water

(These are <u>neutralisation reactions</u>, of course.)

> Acid + Metal Hydroxide → Salt + Water

hydrochloric acid	+	copper oxide	→	copper chloride	+	water
$2HCl$	+	CuO	→	$CuCl_2$	+	H_2O
sulfuric acid	+	potassium hydroxide	→	potassium sulfate	+	water
H_2SO_4	+	$2KOH$	→	K_2SO_4	+	$2H_2O$
nitric acid	+	sodium hydroxide	→	sodium nitrate	+	water
HNO_3	+	$NaOH$	→	$NaNO_3$	+	H_2O
phosphoric acid	+	sodium hydroxide	→	sodium phosphate	+	water
H_3PO_4	+	$3NaOH$	→	Na_3PO_4	+	$3H_2O$

Acids and Carbonates Produce Carbon Dioxide

These are very like the ones above — they just produce <u>carbon dioxide</u> as well.

> Acid + Carbonate → Salt + Water + Carbon dioxide

hydrochloric acid	+	sodium carbonate	→	sodium chloride	+	water	+	carbon dioxide
$2HCl$	+	Na_2CO_3	→	$2NaCl$	+	H_2O	+	CO_2
sulfuric acid	+	calcium carbonate	→	calcium sulfate	+	water	+	carbon dioxide
H_2SO_4	+	$CaCO_3$	→	$CaSO_4$	+	H_2O	+	CO_2
phosphoric acid	+	sodium carbonate	→	sodium phosphate	+	water	+	carbon dioxide
$2H_3PO_4$	+	$3Na_2CO_3$	→	$2Na_3PO_4$	+	$3H_2O$	+	$3CO_2$

Acids and Ammonia Produce Ammonium Salts

And lastly...

> Acid + Ammonia → Ammonium salt

hydrochloric acid	+	ammonia	→	ammonium chloride
HCl	+	NH_3	→	NH_4Cl
sulfuric acid	+	ammonia	→	ammonium sulfate
H_2SO_4	+	$2NH_3$	→	$(NH_4)_2SO_4$
nitric acid	+	ammonia	→	ammonium nitrate
HNO_3	+	NH_3	→	NH_4NO_3

If you're not sure how molecular formulas or balanced equations work, have a look back at pages 8-9. It's really important to know it for this module too.

The last reaction with nitric acid produces the famous <u>ammonium nitrate</u> fertiliser (see pages 40-41).

Acid + Revision → Insomnia Cure...

In the exam you could be asked to give the name of the <u>salt</u> formed when any of the <u>four acids</u> mentioned on this page is added to a <u>metal oxide</u>, <u>hydroxide</u> or <u>carbonate</u>, or <u>ammonia</u>. They might ask you to write a <u>word or symbol equation</u> for the reaction too. Try out lots of different combinations until you understand how all of them work.

Fertilisers

There's a lot more to <u>using fertilisers</u> than making your garden look nice and pretty...

Fertilisers Provide Plants with the Essential Elements for Growth

1) The three main <u>essential</u> elements in fertilisers are <u>nitrogen</u>, <u>phosphorus</u> and <u>potassium</u>. If plants don't get enough of these elements, their <u>growth</u> and <u>life processes</u> are affected.

2) These elements may be <u>missing</u> from the soil if they've been <u>used up</u> by a <u>previous crop</u>.

3) Fertilisers <u>replace</u> these missing elements or provide <u>more</u> of them. This helps to increase the <u>crop yield</u>, as the crops can grow <u>faster</u> and <u>bigger</u>. For example, fertilisers add more <u>nitrogen</u> to <u>plant proteins</u>, which makes the plants <u>grow faster</u>.

4) The fertiliser must first <u>dissolve in water</u> before it can be taken in by the crop <u>roots</u>.

Ammonia Can be Neutralised with Acids to Produce Fertilisers

As you saw on page 39, ammonia is a <u>base</u> and can be <u>neutralised</u> by acids to make <u>ammonium salts</u>. Ammonia is really important to world food production, because it's a <u>key ingredient</u> of many <u>fertilisers</u>.

1) If you neutralise <u>nitric acid</u> with ammonia you get <u>ammonium nitrate</u>. It's an especially good fertiliser because it has <u>nitrogen</u> from <u>two sources</u>, the ammonia and the nitric acid — kind of a <u>double dose</u>.

2) <u>Ammonium sulfate</u> can also be used as a fertiliser. You make it by neutralising <u>sulfuric acid</u> with ammonia.

3) <u>Ammonium phosphate</u> is a fertiliser made by neutralising <u>phosphoric acid</u> with <u>ammonia</u>.

4) <u>Potassium nitrate</u> is also a fertiliser — it can be made by neutralising <u>nitric acid</u> with <u>potassium hydroxide</u>.

Fertilisers are Really Useful — But They Can Cause Big Problems

The <u>population</u> of the world is <u>rising rapidly</u>. Fertilisers <u>increase crop yield</u>, so the more fertiliser we make, the more crops we can grow, and the <u>more people we can feed</u>. But if we use <u>too many</u> fertilisers we risk <u>polluting</u> our <u>water supplies</u> and causing <u>eutrophication</u>.

Fertilisers Damage Lakes and Rivers — Eutrophication

1) When <u>fertiliser</u> is put on fields some of it inevitably <u>runs off</u> and finds its way into <u>rivers and streams</u>.

2) The level of <u>nitrates</u> and <u>phosphates</u> in the river water <u>increases</u>.

3) <u>Algae</u> living in the river water use the nutrients to <u>multiply rapidly</u>, creating an <u>algal bloom</u> (a carpet of algae near the surface of the river). This <u>blocks off the light</u> to the river <u>plants</u> below. The plants cannot photosynthesise, so they have no food and they <u>die</u>.

4) <u>Aerobic bacteria</u> feed on the dead plants and start to <u>multiply</u>. As the bacteria multiply they use up all the <u>oxygen</u> in the water. As a result pretty much <u>everything</u> in the river <u>dies</u> (including fish and insects).

<u>Aerobic</u> just means that they <u>need oxygen</u> to live.

5) This process is called <u>EUTROPHICATION</u>, which basically means '<u>too much of a good thing</u>'.

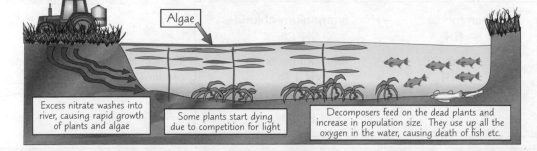

Excess nitrate washes into river, causing rapid growth of plants and algae

Algae

Some plants start dying due to competition for light

Decomposers feed on the dead plants and increase in population size. They use up all the oxygen in the water, causing death of fish etc.

As the picture shows, <u>too many nitrates</u> in the water cause a sequence of '<u>mega-growth</u>', '<u>mega-death</u>' and '<u>mega-decay</u>' involving most of the <u>plant and animal life</u> in the water.

There's nowt wrong wi' just spreadin' muck on it...

Unfortunately, no matter how <u>good</u> something is, there's nearly always a <u>downside</u>. It's a good idea to learn the eutrophication diagram really, really well, and make sure you understand it. Learn it mini-essay style.

Preparing Fertilisers

Ammonium nitrate is a commonly used fertiliser, and you can make it from a few simple chemicals in the lab. If you're going to do real live experiments (like this one) in a chemistry lab, you might want to know how much of the reactants have actually been converted to product, i.e. what the percentage yield of your reaction is.

Preparing Ammonium Nitrate in the Lab

You can make most fertilisers using this titration method — just choose the right acid (nitric, sulfuric or phosphoric) and alkali (ammonia or potassium hydroxide) to get the salt you want. You'll need ammonia and nitric acid to make ammonium nitrate.

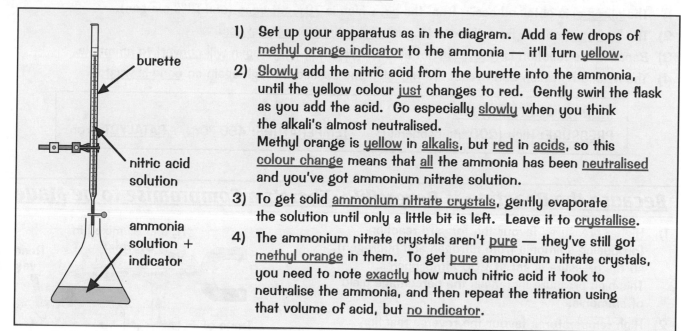

burette

nitric acid solution

ammonia solution + indicator

1) Set up your apparatus as in the diagram. Add a few drops of methyl orange indicator to the ammonia — it'll turn yellow.

2) Slowly add the nitric acid from the burette into the ammonia, until the yellow colour just changes to red. Gently swirl the flask as you add the acid. Go especially slowly when you think the alkali's almost neutralised.
Methyl orange is yellow in alkalis, but red in acids, so this colour change means that all the ammonia has been neutralised and you've got ammonium nitrate solution.

3) To get solid ammonium nitrate crystals, gently evaporate the solution until only a little bit is left. Leave it to crystallise.

4) The ammonium nitrate crystals aren't pure — they've still got methyl orange in them. To get pure ammonium nitrate crystals, you need to note exactly how much nitric acid it took to neutralise the ammonia, and then repeat the titration using that volume of acid, but no indicator.

Percentage Yield Compares Actual with Predicted Yield

> The mass of product that you end up with is called the YIELD of a reaction.

You should realise that in practice you never get a 100% yield, as not all of the reactant will be converted into product. This means that the amount of product will be slightly less than you would expect if it worked absolutely perfectly.

The more reactants you start with, the higher the actual yield will be — that's pretty obvious. But the percentage yield doesn't depend on the amount of reactants you started with — it's a percentage.

- Percentage yield is always somewhere between 0 and 100%.
- 100% yield means that you got all the product you expected to get.
- 0% yield means that no reactants were converted into product, i.e. no product at all was made.
- The predicted yield of a reaction is just the amount of product that you'd get if all the reactant was converted into product.

You can't always get what you want...

Unfortunately, no matter how careful you are, you won't get a 100% yield in any reaction. You'll always get a little loss of product. In industry, people work very hard to keep wastage as low as possible — so reactants that don't react first time are collected and recycled whenever possible. Make sure that you've got the hang of all this, because there's more about it coming up on the next page...

The Haber Process

The Haber process takes nitrogen and hydrogen gas and uses them to make ammonia (NH_3).
It's named after Fritz Haber, the German chemist who developed it, and it's an important industrial process because the ammonia produced is needed for making fertilisers.

The Haber Process is a Reversible Reaction

$$N_2 + 3H_2 \rightleftharpoons 2NH_3$$

A reversible reaction is one that proceeds in both directions.

1) The nitrogen is obtained easily from the air, which is 78% nitrogen (and 21% oxygen).

2) The hydrogen comes from the cracking of oil fractions or natural gas.

3) Because the reaction is reversible not all the nitrogen and hydrogen will convert to ammonia.

4) The N_2 and H_2 which don't react are recycled and passed through again so none is wasted.

INDUSTRIAL CONDITIONS
PRESSURE: High (200 atmospheres);   TEMPERATURE: 450 °C;   CATALYST: Iron

Because the Reaction is Reversible, There's a Compromise to be Made

1) Higher pressures favour the forward reaction (producing ammonia from nitrogen and hydrogen), so the pressure is set at 200 atmospheres. This high pressure increases the percentage yield of ammonia.

2) High temperatures favour the reverse reaction (where ammonia is broken down to give N_2 and H_2) — so high temperature decreases the percentage yield of ammonia.

3) The trouble is, lower temperatures mean slow reaction rates. So manufacturers tend to use high temperatures anyway, to increase the reaction rate.

4) 450 °C is the optimum temperature — it gives a fast reaction rate and a reasonable percentage yield. In other words, it's a compromise — better to wait 20 seconds for a 10% yield than to have to wait 60 seconds for a 20% yield.

5) The unused H_2 and N_2 are recycled, so nothing is wasted.

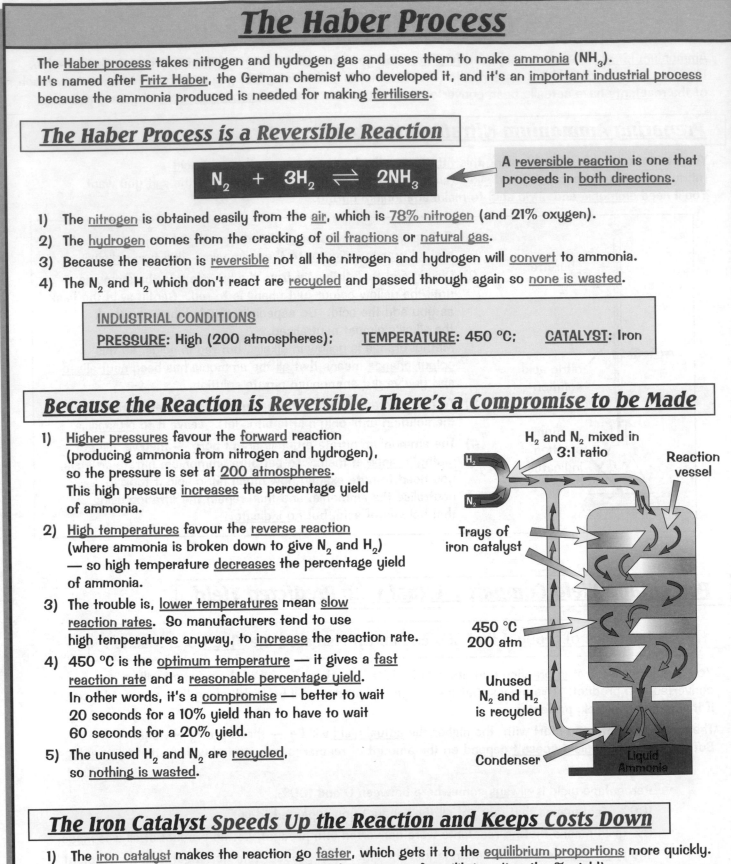

H_2 and N_2 mixed in 3:1 ratio

Reaction vessel

Trays of iron catalyst

450 °C 200 atm

Unused N_2 and H_2 is recycled

Condenser

Liquid Ammonia

The Iron Catalyst Speeds Up the Reaction and Keeps Costs Down

1) The iron catalyst makes the reaction go faster, which gets it to the equilibrium proportions more quickly. But remember, the catalyst doesn't affect the position of equilibrium (i.e. the % yield).

2) Without the catalyst the temperature would have to be raised even further to get a quick enough reaction, and that would reduce the % yield even further. So the catalyst is very important.

200 atmospheres — that could give you a headache...

The Haber process makes ammonia, which is used to make fertilisers, which are great (although they can cause environmental problems too). Because it's a reversible reaction, certain factors need to be controlled to increase the percentage yield. Remember — the temperature is raised to increase speed not yield.

Minimising the Cost of Production

Things like <u>fast reaction rates</u> and <u>high % yields</u> are nice in industry — but in the end, the most important thing is <u>keeping costs down</u>. It all comes down to <u>maximum efficiency</u>...

Production Cost Depends on Several Different Factors

There are <u>five</u> main things that affect the <u>cost</u> of making a new substance. It's these five factors that companies have to consider when deciding <u>if</u>, and then <u>how</u>, to produce a chemical.

1) Price of Energy

a) Industry needs to keep its <u>energy bills</u> as low as possible.

b) If a reaction needs a <u>high temperature</u>, the <u>running costs</u> will be higher.

2) Cost of Raw Materials

a) This is kept to a minimum by <u>recycling</u> any <u>materials</u> that haven't reacted.

b) A good example of this is the <u>Haber process</u>. The % yield of the reaction is quite <u>low</u> (about 10%), but the unreacted N_2 and H_2 can be <u>recycled</u> to keep waste to a minimum.

3) Labour Costs (Wages)

a) Everyone who works for a company has got to be <u>paid</u>.

b) <u>Labour-intensive</u> processes (i.e. those that involve many people), can be very expensive.

c) <u>Automation</u> cuts <u>running costs</u> by reducing the number of people involved.

d) But companies have always got to weigh any <u>savings</u> they make on their <u>wage bill</u> against the <u>initial cost</u> and <u>running costs</u> of the machinery.

4) Plant Costs (Equipment)

a) The cost of equipment depends on the <u>conditions</u> it has to cope with.

b) For example, it costs far more to make something to withstand <u>very high pressures</u> than something which only needs to work at atmospheric pressure.

5) Rate of Production

a) Generally speaking, the <u>faster</u> the reaction goes, the better it is in terms of reducing the time and costs of production.

b) So rates of reaction are often increased by using <u>catalysts</u>.

c) But the increase in production rate has to <u>balance the cost</u> of buying the catalyst in the first place and replacing any that gets lost.

Optimum Conditions are Chosen to Give the Lowest Cost

1) Optimum conditions are those that give the <u>lowest production cost</u> per kg of product — even if this means compromising on the <u>speed of reaction</u> or <u>% yield</u>. Learn the definition:

> <u>OPTIMUM CONDITIONS</u> are those that give the <u>LOWEST PRODUCTION COST</u>.

2) However, the <u>rate of reaction</u> and <u>percentage yield</u> must both be <u>high enough</u> to make a <u>sufficient amount</u> of product each day.

3) Don't forget, a <u>low percentage yield is okay</u>, as long as the starting materials can be recycled.

This will make it as cheap as chips...

In industry, <u>compromises</u> must be made, just like in life, and the Haber process is a prime example of this. You need to learn those <u>five</u> different factors affecting cost, and the definition of 'optimum conditions'. Cover the page and scribble it all down — keep doing it until you get it all right.

Salt

And now for a page all about <u>sodium chloride</u> (<u>NaCl</u>), or <u>salt</u> as it's known to its friends. In <u>hot countries</u> they get salt by pouring <u>sea water</u> into big flat open tanks and letting the <u>Sun</u> evaporate the water, leaving the salt behind. This is no good in a <u>cold country</u> like <u>Britain</u> though — there isn't enough sunshine.

Salt is Mined from Underneath Cheshire

1) In <u>Britain</u> salt is extracted from <u>underground deposits</u> left <u>millions of years</u> ago when <u>ancient seas</u> evaporated. There are huge deposits of this <u>rock salt</u> under <u>Cheshire</u>.

2) Rock salt is a mixture of <u>salt</u> and <u>impurities</u>. It's drilled, blasted and dug out and brought to the surface using machinery.

3) It can also be mined by <u>pumping hot water underground</u>. The <u>salt dissolves</u> and the salt solution is <u>forced to the surface</u> by the pressure of the water — this is called <u>solution mining</u>.

4) When the mining is finished, it's important to <u>fill in the holes</u> in the ground. If not, the land could <u>collapse</u> and <u>slide into the holes</u> — this is called <u>subsidence</u>.

5) Rock salt can be used in its <u>raw state</u> on roads to stop ice forming, or the salt can be separated out and used to preserve or enhance the flavour in <u>food</u> or for <u>making chemicals</u>. If salt's going to be used to make chemicals, usually the first thing they do is electrolyse it using the <u>chlor-alkali process</u>.

Electrolysis of Brine Gives Hydrogen, Chlorine and NaOH

<u>Concentrated brine</u> (sodium chloride solution) is <u>electrolysed</u> industrially using a set-up a bit like this one:

The electrodes are made of an <u>inert</u> material — this is so they won't react with the <u>electrolyte</u> or the <u>products</u> of the electrolysis.

There are <u>three</u> useful products:

a) <u>Hydrogen gas</u> is given off at the (–ve) cathode.

b) <u>Chlorine gas</u> is given off at the (+ve) anode.

c) <u>Sodium hydroxide</u> (NaOH) is formed from the ions left in solution.

These are collected and used to make all sorts of things (see below).

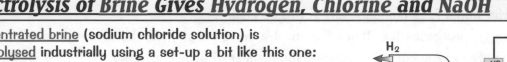

The Half-Equations — Make Sure the Electrons Balance

The sodium chloride solution contains <u>four different ions</u>: Na^+, OH^-, Cl^- and H^+.

1) At the <u>cathode</u>, two hydrogen ions accept one electron each to become <u>one hydrogen molecule</u>.

Cathode: $2H^+ + 2e^- \rightarrow H_2$

2) At the <u>anode</u>, two chloride (Cl^-) ions lose one electron each to become <u>one chlorine molecule</u>.

Anode: $2Cl^- - 2e^- \rightarrow Cl_2$

<u>Oxidation</u> is the <u>loss of electrons</u>, and <u>reduction</u> is the <u>gain of electrons</u>. So the reaction at the <u>anode</u> is an <u>oxidation reaction</u>, and the reaction at the <u>cathode</u> is a <u>reduction reaction</u>.

The Electrolysis of Brine is Done by the Chlor-alkali Industry

1) The <u>products</u> of the chlor-alkali process are used for all kinds of things.

2) For example, the <u>hydrogen</u> gas is used to make <u>ammonia</u> (in the Haber process) and <u>margarine</u>.

3) The <u>chlorine</u> is used to <u>disinfect water</u>, to make <u>plastics</u> (e.g. <u>PVC</u>), <u>solvents</u> or <u>hydrochloric acid</u>.

4) The <u>sodium hydroxide</u> is used to make <u>soap</u>, or can be reacted with <u>chlorine</u> to make <u>household bleach</u>.

5) All of these uses of the <u>products</u> of the electrolysis of brine makes the chlor-alkali industry very important to the economy — lots of <u>new products</u> can be made and lots of <u>jobs</u> are created.

Salt — it's not just for chips any more...

Wowzers — that's an awful lot to learn about salt. Better get cracking, you need to know <u>all</u> of it.

Revision Summary for Module C2

The only way that you can tell if you've learned this module properly is to test yourself. Try these questions, and if there's something you don't know, it means you need to go back and learn it. Even if it's all those equations for the reactions of acids. Don't miss any questions out — you don't get a choice about what comes up on the exam so you need to be sure that you've learnt it all.

1) What is the lithosphere?
2) Briefly describe the inner structure of the Earth.
3) Explain how scientists investigate what lies underneath the Earth's crust.
4) Describe the evidence that backs up Wegener's theory of continental drift.
5) What is meant by 'subduction'?
6) Sketch a labelled diagram showing how a volcano forms.
7) How is an eruption of silica-rich rhyolitic lava different from an eruption of iron-rich basaltic lava?
8) Draw a diagram to show how metamorphic rocks form.
9) Give an example of a metamorphic rock and say what the material it formed from is.
10) Which material is hardest, granite, limestone or marble?
11) How is glass made?
12) How is cement made? What about concrete?
13) Why is reinforced concrete better than non-reinforced concrete as a building material?
14) List three environmental impacts of extracting rocks from the Earth.
15) Draw and label the apparatus used to purify copper. Label the anode, the cathode and the electrolyte.
16) During the purification process, which electrode gets bigger — the cathode or the anode?
    Write down the equation for the reaction at the anode, and the equation for the reaction at the cathode.
17) Give an example of a large-scale use of each of the following: brass, solder, amalgam.
18) What two metals is brass made from? How are its physical properties different from those metals?
19) Give an example of a smart alloy. What is it used for?
20) Write down the word equation for the corrosion of iron.
21) Explain why a car parked on the Brighton seafront rusts more than a car parked in hot, dry Cairo.
22) Why doesn't aluminium corrode when it's wet?
23) Give two advantages of using aluminium instead of steel for car bodywork.
24) Polypropylene fibres are cheap and hard-wearing. What might they be used for when building a car?
25) What are acids and bases? What is an alkali?
26) What type of ions are always present when: a) acids, and b) alkalis dissolve in water?
27) Write the equation of a neutralisation reaction in terms of these ions.
28)* Write a word equation for the reaction between phosphoric acid and potassium hydroxide.
29)* Write a balanced symbol equation for the reaction between sulfuric acid and sodium carbonate.
30) Write a balanced symbol equation for the reaction between nitric acid and ammonia.
31) Name three essential elements in fertilisers.
32) How does nitrogen increase the growth of plants?
33) Name two fertilisers which are manufactured from ammonia.
34) Describe what can happen if too much fertiliser is put onto fields.
35) Describe how you could produce ammonium nitrate in the lab.
36) Explain why 450 °C is used as the operating temperature for the Haber process.
37) What effect does the catalyst have on the Haber process reaction?
38) Give five factors that affect the cost of producing a chemical on an industrial scale.
39) Describe two ways that salt can be mined.
40) What are the three main products of brine electrolysis?

*Answers on page 108.

Energy Transfer in Reactions

Chemical reactions can either <u>release</u> heat energy, or <u>take in</u> heat energy.

Combustion is an Exothermic Reaction — Heat's Given Out

An <u>EXOTHERMIC REACTION</u> is one which <u>GIVES OUT ENERGY</u> to the surroundings, usually in the form of <u>HEAT</u>, which is shown by a <u>RISE IN TEMPERATURE</u>.

The best example of an <u>exothermic</u> reaction is <u>burning fuels</u>.
This obviously <u>gives out a lot of heat</u> — it's very exothermic.

In an Endothermic Reaction, Heat is Taken In

An <u>ENDOTHERMIC REACTION</u> is one which <u>TAKES IN ENERGY</u> from the surroundings, usually in the form of <u>HEAT</u>, which is shown by a <u>FALL IN TEMPERATURE</u>.

Endothermic reactions are <u>less common</u> and less easy to spot. One example is <u>thermal decomposition</u>. Heat must be supplied to cause the compound to <u>decompose</u>, e.g. decomposition of $CuCO_3$ (see p. 70).

Temperature Changes Help Decide If a Reaction's Exo or Endo

1) You can measure the amount of <u>energy produced</u> by a <u>chemical reaction</u> (in solution) by taking the <u>temperature of the reactants</u>, <u>mixing</u> them in a <u>polystyrene cup</u> and measuring the <u>temperature of the solution</u> at the <u>end</u> of the reaction. Easy.

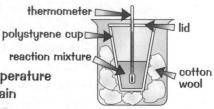

2) Adding an <u>acid to an alkali</u> is an <u>exothermic</u> reaction. Measure the temperature of the alkali before you add the acid, then measure the temperature again after adding the acid and mixing — you'll see an <u>increase in temperature</u>.

3) Dissolving <u>ammonium nitrate</u> in water is an endothermic reaction. Adding a couple of spatulas of ammonium nitrate to a polystyrene cup of water results in a <u>drop in temperature</u>.

Energy Must Always be Supplied to Break Bonds... ...and Energy is Always Released When Bonds Form

1) During a chemical reaction, <u>old bonds are broken</u> and <u>new bonds are formed</u>.

2) Energy must be <u>supplied</u> to break <u>existing bonds</u> — so bond breaking is an <u>endothermic</u> process.

3) Energy is <u>released</u> when new bonds are <u>formed</u> — so bond formation is an <u>exothermic</u> process.

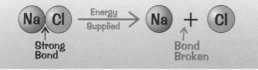

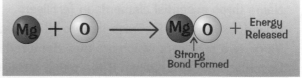

4) In an <u>exothermic</u> reaction, the energy <u>released</u> in bond formation is <u>greater</u> than the energy used in <u>breaking</u> old bonds.

5) In an <u>endothermic</u> reaction, the energy <u>required</u> to break old bonds is <u>greater</u> than the energy <u>released</u> when <u>new bonds</u> are formed.

Chemistry in "real-world application" shocker...

When you see <u>Stevie Gerrard</u> hobble off the pitch and press a bag to his leg, he's using an <u>endothermic reaction</u>. The cold pack contains an inner bag full of water and an outer one full of ammonium nitrate. When he presses the pack the inner bag <u>breaks</u> and they <u>mix together</u>. The ammonium nitrate dissolves in the water and, as this is an endothermic reaction, it <u>draws in heat</u> from Stevie's injured leg.

Measuring the Energy Content of Fuels

Different fuels give out <u>different amounts of energy</u> when they burn. Here's how you measure that energy...

Use Specific Heat Capacity to Calculate Energy Transferred

1) This "<u>calorimetric</u>" experiment involves <u>heating water</u> by burning a <u>liquid fuel</u>.

2) If you measure (i) how <u>much fuel</u> you've burned and (ii) the <u>temperature change</u> of the water, you can work out how much energy is supplied by <u>each gram of fuel</u>.

3) You also need to know water's <u>specific heat capacity</u> — this is the <u>amount of energy</u> needed to raise the temperature of <u>1 gram</u> of water by <u>1 °C</u>. The specific heat capacity of <u>water</u> is <u>4.2 J/g/°C</u> — so it takes 4.2 joules of energy to raise the temperature of 1 g of water by 1 °C.

4) If you do the same experiment with <u>different fuels</u>, you can compare their <u>energy transferred per gram</u>. If a fuel has a <u>higher</u> energy content per gram, you need <u>less fuel</u> to cause the <u>same temperature rise</u>.

Calorimetric Method — Reduce Heat Loss as Much as Possible

1) It's dead important to make as much heat as possible go into <u>heating up</u> the water. <u>Reducing draughts</u> is the key here — use a <u>screen</u> to act as a draught excluder (and don't do it next to an open window).

2) Put some <u>fuel</u> into a <u>spirit burner</u> (or use a <u>bottled gas burner</u> if the fuel is a gas) and <u>weigh</u> the burner <u>full of fuel</u>.

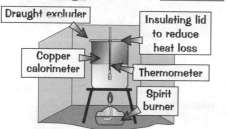

Draught excluder
Insulating lid to reduce heat loss
Copper calorimeter
Thermometer
Spirit burner

3) Measure out, say, 200 cm³ of water (this is the same as 200 g of water) into a <u>copper calorimeter</u>.

4) Take the <u>initial temperature</u> of the water — then put the burner <u>under</u> the calorimeter and <u>light the wick</u>.

5) When the heat from the burner has made the water <u>temperature rise</u> by <u>20-30 °C</u>, blow out the spirit burner and make a note of the <u>highest</u> temperature the water reaches.

6) <u>Reweigh</u> the burner and fuel.

7) If you're comparing two fuels, repeat the procedure with the second fuel.

Three Calculations to Find the Energy Output Per Gram of Fuel

1) You find the <u>mass of fuel burned</u> by <u>subtracting</u> the <u>final mass</u> of fuel and burner from the <u>initial mass</u> of fuel and burner. Simple.

2) The amount of <u>energy transferred</u> to the water is given by:

| ENERGY TRANSFERRED (in J) | = | MASS OF WATER (in g) | × | SPECIFIC HEAT CAPACITY OF WATER (= 4.2 J/g °C) | × | TEMPERATURE CHANGE (in °C) |

Which can also be written like this:

$$\text{Energy transferred} = m \times c \times \Delta T$$

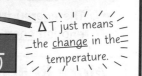

ΔT just means the <u>change</u> in the temperature.

3) Then the <u>energy</u> given out <u>per gram of fuel</u> is given by:

$$\text{ENERGY GIVEN OUT PER GRAM (in J/g)} = \frac{\text{ENERGY RELEASED (in J)}}{\text{MASS OF FUEL BURNED (in g)}}$$

Make It a Fair Test by Keeping Conditions the Same

1) To <u>compare</u> the energy content of different fuels you need to do the <u>same experiment</u> several times, but using a <u>different fuel</u> in the burner each time.

2) For the comparison to be <u>fair</u>, <u>everything</u> (except the fuel used) should be the <u>same</u>.

3) This means that: (i) you should use the <u>same apparatus</u>, (ii) you should use the <u>same amount of water</u> each time, (iii) the water should <u>start</u> and <u>finish</u> at the <u>same temperature</u> each time.

4) In order for the results to be <u>reliable</u> you would have to <u>repeat</u> the experiment several times and discount any <u>anomalous</u> results.

Hope you've got the energy to revise all this...

In the exam they might give you <u>data</u> from simple calorimetric experiments involving the combustion of fuel to compare, and you'll have to use it to say which fuel releases the <u>most energy</u>. Pretty easy.

Chemical Reaction Rates

The rate of a chemical reaction is how fast the reactants are changed into products (the reaction is over when one of the reactants is completely used up). People working in the chemical industry like to know what affects the rate of a reaction — because the faster you make chemicals, the faster you make money.

Reactions Can Go at All Sorts of Different Rates

1) One of the slowest is the rusting of iron (it's not slow enough though — what about my little MGB).

2) Other slow reactions include chemical weathering — like acid rain damage to limestone buildings.

3) An example of a moderate speed reaction is a metal (e.g. magnesium) reacting with dilute acid to produce a gentle stream of bubbles.

4) Burning is a fast reaction, but an explosion is really fast and releases a lot of gas. Explosive reactions are all over in a fraction of a second.

You Can Do an Experiment to Follow a Reaction

The rate of a reaction that produces a gas can be observed by measuring how quickly the gas is produced. There are two ways of doing this:

MEASURE THE CHANGE IN MASS

If you carry out the reaction on a balance, the mass will fall as the gas is released. You need to take readings of the mass at regular time intervals.

MEASURE THE VOLUME OF GAS GIVEN OFF

This method is pretty similar, except you use a gas syringe to measure the volume of gas given off after regular time intervals.

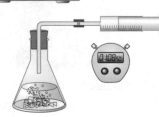

Whichever of these methods you use, you can plot your results on a graph. P.50 shows you the type of graph you'll get and what it shows.

Particles Must Collide with Enough Energy in Order to React

Reaction rates are explained perfectly by collision theory. It's simple really.
The rate of a chemical reaction depends on:

- The collision frequency of reacting particles (how often they collide). The more collisions there are the faster the reaction is.

- The energy transferred during a collision. Particles have to collide with enough energy for the collision to be successful.

A successful collision is a collision that ends in the particles reacting to form products.

More Reactant Used Means More Product Formed

1) The amount of product you get from a reaction (the yield) depends on the amount of reactant you start with.

2) More reactant means more particles. These particles go on to have more reactions so create more product.

3) The amount of product you get is directly proportional to the amount of limiting reactant (the reactant that's totally used up). For example, if you half the particles of limiting reactant, you get half the yield.

4) Once all of the limiting reactant is used up, the reaction can't continue and you can't get any more product.

5) There might still be some of the other reactant left at the end — we say this reactant is in excess.

Get a fast, furious reaction — tickle your teacher...

First off... remember that the amount of product you get is proportional to the amount of limiting reactant you start with. So all the stuff about the rate of a reaction is only talking about how quickly your products form — not how much of them you get. It's an important difference — so get your head round it asap.

Collision Theory

The rate of a reaction depends on <u>four</u> things — <u>temperature</u>, <u>concentration</u> (or <u>pressure</u> for gases), the presence of a <u>catalyst</u> and the <u>size of the particles</u>. This page explains <u>why</u> these things affect the reaction rate.

More Collisions Increases the Rate of Reaction

Reactions happen if <u>particles collide</u>. So if you <u>increase</u> the <u>number</u> of collisions, the reaction happens <u>more quickly</u>. The four factors below all lead to more collisions... (Well, a catalyst's a bit different, I guess — there are the same number of collisions, it's just that more of them lead to a reaction.)

1) Increasing the Temperature Means the Particles are Going Faster and have More Energy

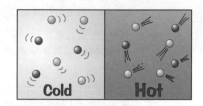
Cold   Hot

When the <u>temperature is increased</u> the particles all <u>move quicker</u>. If they're moving quicker, they're going to have <u>more collisions</u>.

Higher temperatures also increase the <u>energy of the collisions</u>, since the particles are moving <u>faster</u>. Reactions <u>only happen</u> if the particles collide with <u>enough energy</u>. At a <u>higher temperature</u> there'll be <u>more particles</u> colliding with <u>enough energy</u> to make the reaction happen.

2) Increasing the Concentration (or Pressure) Means the Particles are More Crowded Together

Low Concentration   High Concentration
(Low Pressure)   (High Pressure)

If a solution is made more <u>concentrated</u> it means there are more particles of <u>reactant</u> in the same volume, which makes collisions <u>more likely</u>. In a <u>gas</u>, increasing the <u>pressure</u> means the molecules are <u>more crowded</u>, so the frequency of the collisions <u>increases</u>.

3) Smaller Solid Particles (or More Surface Area) Means Other Particles Can Get to It More Easily

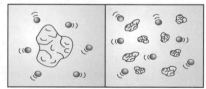

If one of the reactants is a <u>solid</u> then <u>breaking it up</u> into <u>smaller</u> pieces will <u>increase its surface area</u>. This means the particles around it will have <u>more area to work on</u> so the frequency of collisions will <u>increase</u>. For example, soluble pain killers dissolve faster when they're broken into bits.

<u>Fine powders</u> of <u>combustible materials</u> dispersed in the air burn very very fast because they have such a <u>big surface area</u>. In fact, if there's a spark, they'll <u>EXPLODE</u> (an explosion is basically a very fast reaction that releases a lot of gaseous products very quickly). That's why factories that make <u>custard powder</u>, <u>flour</u> and powdered <u>sulfur</u> have to be careful.

4) A Catalyst Increases the Number of Successful Collisions

A <u>catalyst</u> is a substance which increases the <u>speed of a reaction</u>, <u>without</u> being chemically changed or used up in the reaction — and because it isn't used up, you only need a <u>tiny bit</u> of it to catalyse large amounts of reactants. Catalysts tend to be very <u>fussy</u> about which reactions they catalyse though — you can't just stick any old catalyst in a reaction and expect it to work.

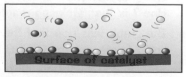
Surface of catalyst

A catalyst works by giving the reacting particles a <u>surface</u> to stick to where they can bump into each other — and <u>reduces the energy needed</u> by the particles before they react. So the <u>overall number</u> of collisions isn't increased, but the number of <u>successful collisions</u> is.

Collision theory — it's always the other driver...

Industries that use chemical reactions to make their products have to think <u>carefully</u> about reaction rates. <u>Ideally</u>, they want to <u>speed up</u> the reaction to get the products quickly, but high temperatures and pressures are <u>expensive</u>. So they <u>compromise</u> — they use a <u>slower</u> reaction but a <u>cheaper</u> one.

Rate of Reaction Data

In the exam they might ask you to interpret <u>rate of reaction data</u>. Read on...

Reaction Rate Graphs Show Rate of Reaction Data

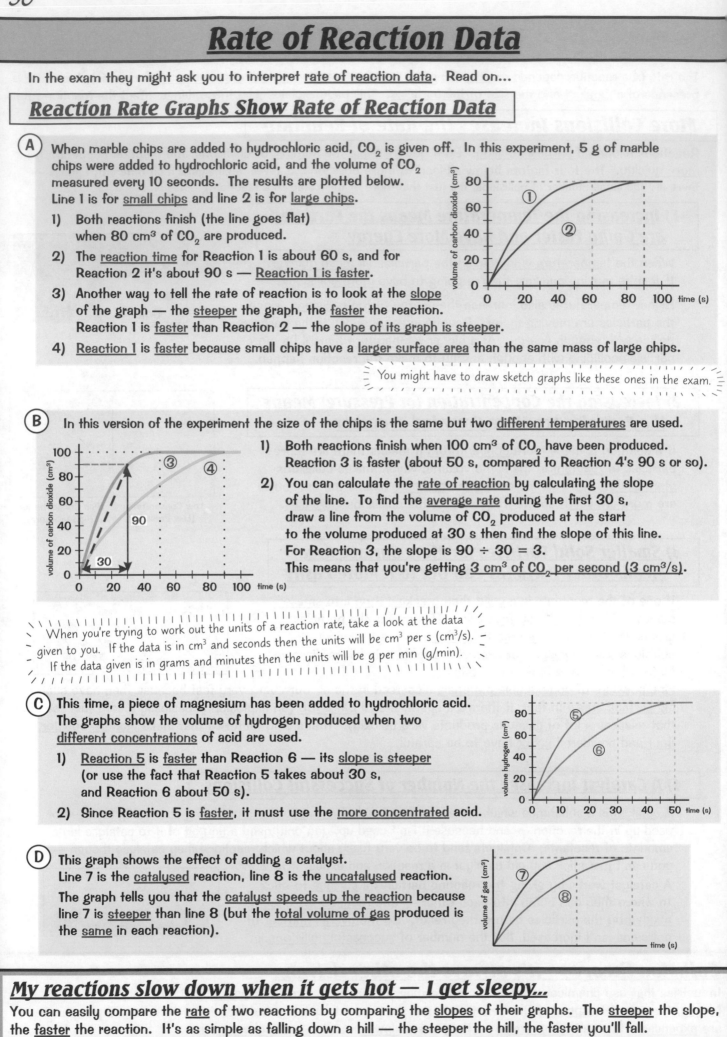

(A) When marble chips are added to hydrochloric acid, CO_2 is given off. In this experiment, 5 g of marble chips were added to hydrochloric acid, and the volume of CO_2 measured every 10 seconds. The results are plotted below. Line 1 is for <u>small chips</u> and line 2 is for <u>large chips</u>.

1) Both reactions finish (the line goes flat) when 80 cm³ of CO_2 are produced.

2) The <u>reaction time</u> for Reaction 1 is about 60 s, and for Reaction 2 it's about 90 s — <u>Reaction 1 is faster</u>.

3) Another way to tell the rate of reaction is to look at the <u>slope</u> of the graph — the <u>steeper</u> the graph, the <u>faster</u> the reaction. Reaction 1 is <u>faster</u> than Reaction 2 — the <u>slope of its graph is steeper</u>.

4) <u>Reaction 1</u> is <u>faster</u> because small chips have a <u>larger surface area</u> than the same mass of large chips.

You might have to draw sketch graphs like these ones in the exam.

(B) In this version of the experiment the size of the chips is the same but two <u>different temperatures</u> are used.

1) Both reactions finish when 100 cm³ of CO_2 have been produced. Reaction 3 is faster (about 50 s, compared to Reaction 4's 90 s or so).

2) You can calculate the <u>rate of reaction</u> by calculating the slope of the line. To find the <u>average rate</u> during the first 30 s, draw a line from the volume of CO_2 produced at the start to the volume produced at 30 s then find the slope of this line. For Reaction 3, the slope is 90 ÷ 30 = 3. This means that you're getting <u>3 cm³ of CO_2 per second (3 cm³/s)</u>.

When you're trying to work out the units of a reaction rate, take a look at the data given to you. If the data is in cm³ and seconds then the units will be cm³ per s (cm³/s). If the data given is in grams and minutes then the units will be g per min (g/min).

(C) This time, a piece of magnesium has been added to hydrochloric acid. The graphs show the volume of hydrogen produced when two <u>different concentrations</u> of acid are used.

1) <u>Reaction 5</u> is <u>faster</u> than Reaction 6 — its <u>slope is steeper</u> (or use the fact that Reaction 5 takes about 30 s, and Reaction 6 about 50 s).

2) Since Reaction 5 is <u>faster</u>, it must use the <u>more concentrated</u> acid.

(D) This graph shows the effect of adding a catalyst. Line 7 is the <u>catalysed</u> reaction, line 8 is the <u>uncatalysed</u> reaction.

The graph tells you that the <u>catalyst speeds up the reaction</u> because line 7 is <u>steeper</u> than line 8 (but the <u>total volume of gas</u> produced is the <u>same</u> in each reaction).

My reactions slow down when it gets hot — I get sleepy...

You can easily compare the <u>rate</u> of two reactions by comparing the <u>slopes</u> of their graphs. The <u>steeper</u> the slope, the <u>faster</u> the reaction. It's as simple as falling down a hill — the steeper the hill, the faster you'll fall.

Reacting Masses

The biggest trouble with <u>relative atomic mass</u> and <u>relative formula mass</u> is that they <u>sound</u> so blood-curdling. They're very important though, so take a few deep breaths, and just enjoy, as the mists slowly clear...

Relative Atomic Mass, A_r — Easy Peasy

In the periodic table, the elements all have <u>two</u> numbers.
The <u>bigger one</u> is the <u>relative atomic mass</u>.

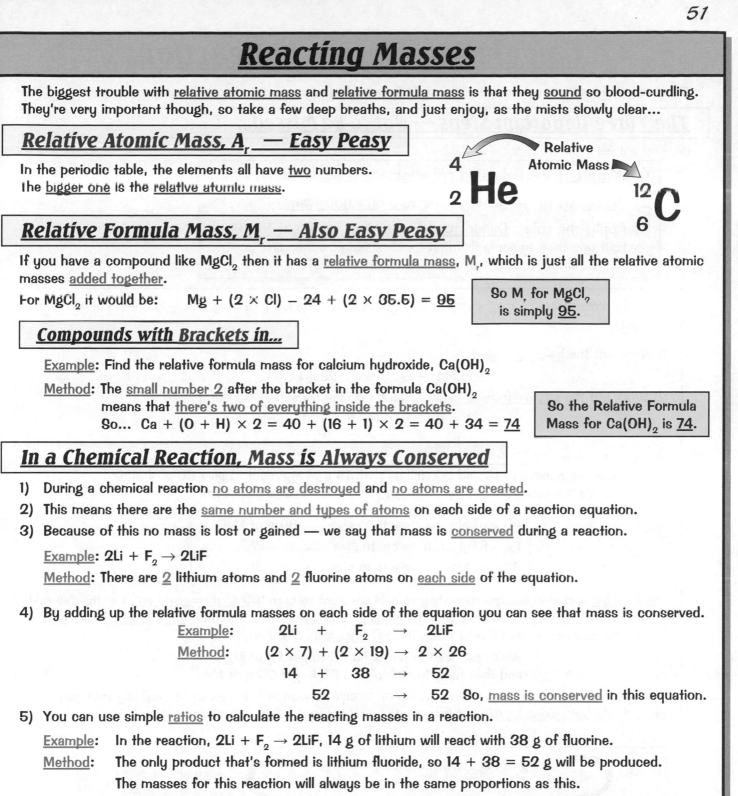

Relative Atomic Mass

$_2^4\text{He}$ $_6^{12}\text{C}$

Relative Formula Mass, M_r — Also Easy Peasy

If you have a compound like $MgCl_2$ then it has a <u>relative formula mass</u>, M_r, which is just all the relative atomic masses <u>added together</u>.

For $MgCl_2$ it would be: $Mg + (2 \times Cl) = 24 + (2 \times 35.5) = \underline{95}$

So M_r for $MgCl_2$ is simply <u>95</u>.

Compounds with Brackets in...

<u>Example</u>: Find the relative formula mass for calcium hydroxide, $Ca(OH)_2$

<u>Method</u>: The <u>small number 2</u> after the bracket in the formula $Ca(OH)_2$ means that <u>there's two of everything inside the brackets</u>.
So... $Ca + (O + H) \times 2 = 40 + (16 + 1) \times 2 = 40 + 34 = \underline{74}$

So the Relative Formula Mass for $Ca(OH)_2$ is <u>74</u>.

In a Chemical Reaction, Mass is Always Conserved

1) During a chemical reaction <u>no atoms are destroyed</u> and <u>no atoms are created</u>.

2) This means there are the <u>same number and types of atoms</u> on each side of a reaction equation.

3) Because of this no mass is lost or gained — we say that mass is <u>conserved</u> during a reaction.

   <u>Example</u>: $2Li + F_2 \rightarrow 2LiF$
   <u>Method</u>: There are <u>2</u> lithium atoms and <u>2</u> fluorine atoms on <u>each side</u> of the equation.

4) By adding up the relative formula masses on each side of the equation you can see that mass is conserved.

   <u>Example</u>: $2Li$ + F_2 $\rightarrow$ $2LiF$
   <u>Method</u>: $(2 \times 7) + (2 \times 19) \rightarrow 2 \times 26$
   $$14 + 38 \rightarrow 52$$
   $$52 \rightarrow 52 \quad \text{So, } \underline{\text{mass is conserved}} \text{ in this equation.}$$

5) You can use simple <u>ratios</u> to calculate the reacting masses in a reaction.

   <u>Example</u>:   In the reaction, $2Li + F_2 \rightarrow 2LiF$, 14 g of lithium will react with 38 g of fluorine.
   <u>Method</u>:   The only product that's formed is lithium fluoride, so $14 + 38 = 52$ g will be produced.
   The masses for this reaction will always be in the same proportions as this.
   Multiplying or dividing these masses by the same number gives you other sets of reacting masses.

Element / compound in reaction	Lithium	Fluorine	Lithium fluoride
Original reacting masses	14 g	38 g	52 g
Reacting masses set 2	$14 \div 2 = 7$ g	$38 \div 2 = 19$ g	$52 \div 2 = 26$ g
Reacting masses set 3	$14 \times 1.5 = 21$ g	$38 \times 1.5 = 57$ g	$52 \times 1.5 = 78$ g

Phew, Chemistry — scary stuff sometimes, innit...

This page is <u>really important</u>... You've gotta remember that in a reaction <u>no mass is lost</u> and <u>no mass is gained</u>. Otherwise you'll be messing with the first law of thermodynamics — and you wouldn't want that, would you..

Calculating Masses in Reactions

These can be kinda scary too, but chill out, little trembling one — just relax and enjoy.

The Three Important Steps — Not to Be Missed...

(Miss one out and it'll all go horribly wrong, believe me.)

1) Write out the balanced equation

2) Work out M_r — just for the two bits you want

3) Apply the rule: Divide to get one, then multiply to get all
   (But you have to apply this first to the substance they give
   information about, and then the other one!)

Don't worry — these steps should all make sense when you look at the example below.

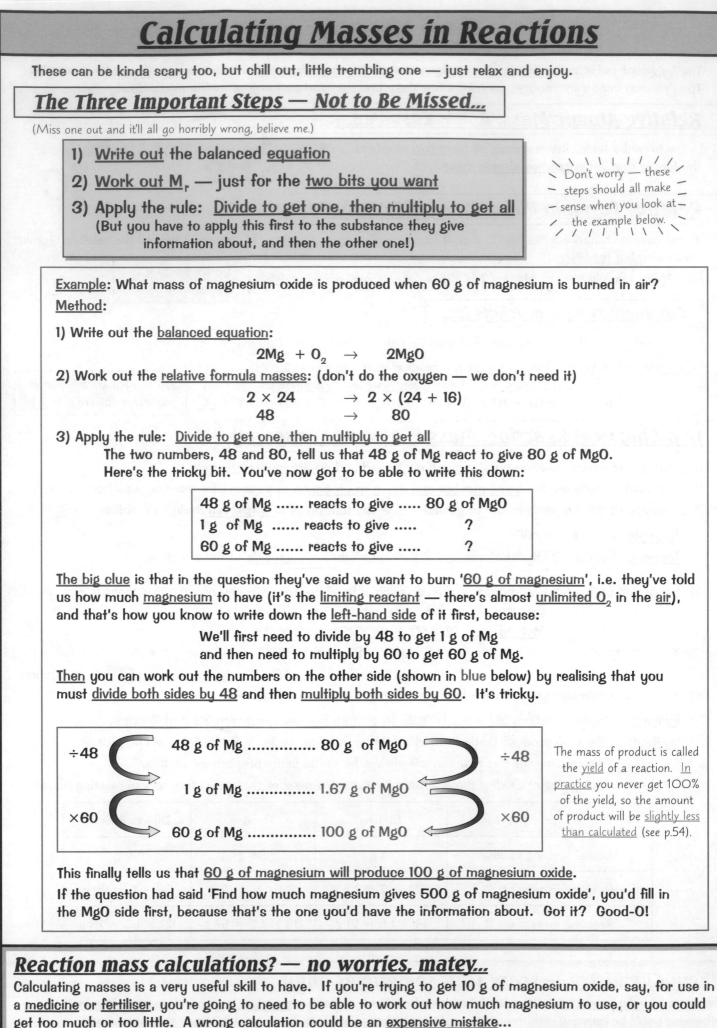

Example: What mass of magnesium oxide is produced when 60 g of magnesium is burned in air?

Method:

1) Write out the balanced equation:

$$2Mg + O_2 \rightarrow 2MgO$$

2) Work out the relative formula masses: (don't do the oxygen — we don't need it)

$$2 \times 24 \qquad \rightarrow \quad 2 \times (24 + 16)$$
$$48 \qquad \rightarrow \qquad 80$$

3) Apply the rule: Divide to get one, then multiply to get all

The two numbers, 48 and 80, tell us that 48 g of Mg react to give 80 g of MgO.
Here's the tricky bit. You've now got to be able to write this down:

> 48 g of Mg ...... reacts to give ..... 80 g of MgO
> 1 g of Mg ...... reacts to give ..... ?
> 60 g of Mg ...... reacts to give ..... ?

The big clue is that in the question they've said we want to burn '60 g of magnesium', i.e. they've told us how much magnesium to have (it's the limiting reactant — there's almost unlimited O_2 in the air), and that's how you know to write down the left-hand side of it first, because:

> We'll first need to divide by 48 to get 1 g of Mg
> and then need to multiply by 60 to get 60 g of Mg.

Then you can work out the numbers on the other side (shown in blue below) by realising that you must divide both sides by 48 and then multiply both sides by 60. It's tricky.

> ÷48   48 g of Mg .... 80 g of MgO   ÷48
>
> 1 g of Mg .... 1.67 g of MgO
>
> ×60   60 g of Mg .... 100 g of MgO   ×60

The mass of product is called the yield of a reaction. In practice you never get 100% of the yield, so the amount of product will be slightly less than calculated (see p.54).

This finally tells us that 60 g of magnesium will produce 100 g of magnesium oxide.

If the question had said 'Find how much magnesium gives 500 g of magnesium oxide', you'd fill in the MgO side first, because that's the one you'd have the information about. Got it? Good-O!

Reaction mass calculations? — no worries, matey...

Calculating masses is a very useful skill to have. If you're trying to get 10 g of magnesium oxide, say, for use in a medicine or fertiliser, you're going to need to be able to work out how much magnesium to use, or you could get too much or too little. A wrong calculation could be an expensive mistake...

Atom Economy

It's important in industrial reactions that as much of the reactants as possible get turned into useful products. This depends on the <u>atom economy</u> and the <u>percentage yield</u> (see next page) of the reaction.

"Atom Economy" — % of Reactants Changed to Useful Products

1) A lot of reactions make <u>more than one product</u>. Some of them will be <u>useful</u>, but others will just be <u>waste</u>, e.g. when you make quicklime from limestone, you also get CO_2 as a waste product

2) The <u>atom economy</u> of a reaction tells you how much of the <u>mass</u> of the reactants is wasted when manufacturing a chemical. <u>Learn</u> the equation:

$$\text{atom economy} = \frac{\text{total } M_r \text{ of desired products}}{\text{total } M_r \text{ of all products}} \times 100$$

3) <u>100%</u> atom economy means that <u>all</u> the atoms in the reactants have been turned into <u>useful</u> (desired) <u>products</u>. The <u>higher</u> the atom economy the '<u>greener</u>' the process.

> **Example:** Hydrogen gas is made on a large scale by reacting natural gas (methane) with steam.
>
> $$CH_4(g) + H_2O(g) \rightarrow CO(g) + 3H_2(g)$$
>
> Calculate the atom economy of this reaction.

Method:
1) Identify the useful product — that's the hydrogen gas.
2) Work out the M_r of all the products and the useful product:

CO	$3H_2$	$3H_2$
12 + 16	3 × (2 × 1)	3 × (2 × 1)
34		6

3) Use the formula to calculate the atom economy: atom economy $= \dfrac{6}{34} \times 100 = \underline{17.6\%}$

So in this reaction, <u>over 80%</u> of the starting materials are <u>wasted</u>.

High Atom Economy is Better for Profits and the Environment

1) Pretty obviously, if you're making <u>lots of waste</u>, that's a <u>problem</u>.

2) Reactions with low atom economy <u>use up resources</u> very quickly. At the same time, they make lots of <u>waste</u> materials that have to be <u>disposed</u> of somehow. That tends to make these reactions <u>unsustainable</u> — the raw materials will run out and the waste has to go somewhere.

3) For the same reasons, low atom economy reactions aren't usually <u>profitable</u>. Raw materials are <u>expensive to buy</u>, and waste products can be expensive to <u>remove</u> and dispose of <u>responsibly</u>.

4) The best way around the problem is to find a <u>use</u> for the waste products rather than just <u>throwing them away</u>. There's often <u>more than one way</u> to make the product you want, so the trick is to come up with a reaction that gives <u>useful "by-products"</u> rather than useless ones.

5) The reactions with the <u>highest</u> atom economy are the ones that only have <u>one product</u>. Those reactions have an atom economy of <u>100%</u>.

<u>Atom economy — important but not the whole story...</u>

You could get asked about <u>any</u> industrial reaction in the exam. Don't panic — whatever example they give you, the <u>same stuff</u> applies. In the real world, high atom economy isn't enough, though. You need to think about the <u>percentage yield</u> of the reaction (next page) and the <u>energy cost</u> as well.

Percentage Yield

Percentage yield tells you about the <u>overall success</u> of an experiment. It compares what you think you should get (<u>predicted yield</u>) with what you get in practice (<u>actual yield</u>).

Percentage Yield Compares Actual and Predicted Yield

The more reactants you start with, the higher the <u>actual yield</u> will be — that's pretty obvious. But the <u>percentage yield doesn't</u> depend on the amount of reactants you started with — it's a <u>percentage</u>.

1) The <u>predicted yield</u> of a reaction can be calculated from the <u>balanced reaction equation</u> (see page 52).

2) Percentage yield is given by the formula:

$$\text{percentage yield} = \frac{\text{actual yield (grams)}}{\text{predicted yield (grams)}} \times 100$$

3) Percentage yield is <u>always</u> somewhere between 0 and 100%.

4) 100% yield means that you got <u>all</u> the product you expected to get.

5) 0% yield means that <u>no</u> reactants were converted into product, i.e. no product at all was <u>made</u>.

6) Industrial processes want as <u>high</u> a percentage yield as possible to <u>reduce waste</u> and <u>reduce costs</u>.

Yields are Always Less Than 100%

In real life, you <u>never</u> get a 100% yield. Some product or reactant <u>always</u> gets lost along the way — and that goes for big <u>industrial processes</u> as well as school lab experiments.

How this happens depends on <u>what sort of reaction</u> it is and what <u>apparatus</u> is being used.

Lots of things can go wrong, but the four you need to <u>know about</u> are:

1) Evaporation

Liquids evaporate <u>all the time</u> — and even more so while they're being heated.

Liquid evaporating...

2) Not All Reactants React to Make a Product

In <u>reversible reactions</u>, the products can <u>turn back</u> into reactants, so the yield will <u>never</u> be <u>100%</u>.

BOTH WAYS

For example, in the Haber process, at the same time as the reaction $N_2 + 3H_2 \rightarrow 2NH_3$ is taking place, the <u>reverse</u> reaction $2NH_3 \rightarrow N_2 + 3H_2$ is <u>also</u> happening.

3) Filtration

When you <u>filter a liquid</u> to remove <u>solid particles</u>, you nearly always lose a bit of liquid or a bit of solid.

- If you want to <u>keep the liquid</u>, you lose the bit that remains with the solid and filter paper (as they always stay a bit wet).

- If you want to <u>keep the solid</u>, some of it usually gets left behind when you scrape it off the filter paper — even if you're really careful.

4) Transferring Liquids

You always lose a bit of liquid when you <u>transfer</u> it from one container to another — even if you manage not to spill it.

Some of it always gets left behind on the <u>inside surface</u> of the old container. Think about it — it's always wet when you finish.

LIQUID NITROGEN

You can't always get what you want...

Unfortunately, no matter how careful you are, you're not going to get a 100% yield in any reaction. So you'll <u>always</u> get a little loss of product. In industry, people work very hard to keep wastage as <u>low</u> as possible — so <u>reactants</u> that don't react first time are <u>collected</u> and <u>recycled</u> whenever possible.

Chemical Production

There are lots of ways you could manufacture drugs — it all depends on how much you want to make.

The Type of Manufacturing Process Depends on the Product

Batch Production Only Operates at Certain Times

Pharmaceutical drugs are complicated to make and there's fairly low demand for them. Batch production is often the most cost-effective way to produce small quantities of different drugs to order, because:

1) It's flexible — several different products can be made using the same equipment.

2) Start-up costs are relatively low — small-scale, multi-purpose equipment can be bought off the shelf.

But batch production does have disadvantages:

1) It's labour-intensive — the equipment needs to be set up and manually controlled for each batch and then cleaned out at the end.

2) It can be tricky to keep the same quality from batch to batch.

Continuous Production Runs All the Time

Large-scale industrial manufacture of popular chemicals, e.g. the Haber process for making ammonia uses continuous production because:

1) Production never stops, so you don't waste time emptying the reactor and setting it up again.

2) It runs automatically — you only need to interfere if something goes wrong.

3) The quality of the product is very consistent.

But, start-up costs to build the plant are huge, and it isn't cost-effective to run at less than full capacity.

Pharmaceutical Drugs Often Cost A Lot — For Several Reasons

1) Research and Development — finding a suitable compound, testing it, modifying it, testing again, until it's ready. This involves the work of lots of highly paid scientists.

2) Trialling — no drug can be sold until it's gone through loads of time-consuming tests including animal trials and human trials. The manufacturer has to prove that the drug meets legal requirements so it works and it's safe.

3) Manufacture — multi-step batch production is labour-intensive and can't be automated. Other costs include energy and raw materials. The raw materials for pharmaceuticals are often rare and sometimes need to be extracted from plants (an expensive process).

> It takes about 12 years and £900 million to develop a new drug and get it onto the market. Ouch.

To extract a substance from a plant, it has to be crushed then boiled and dissolved in a suitable solvent. Then, you can extract the substance you want by chromatography.

Crush

Boil to dissolve in a suitable solvent

Separate by chromatography

Spots of different chemicals move up the paper at different speeds

Dissolved substance

Solvent

Extract the chemical you want

Cut out the right blob and dissolve it off the paper

Discard the impurities

Test For Purity Using Chromatography And Boiling and Melting Points

You might be given data on a purity test and asked what it shows. Don't worry, it's fairly straightforward.

1) Pure substances won't be separated by chromatography — it'll all move as one blob.

2) Pure substances have a specific melting point and boiling point (e.g. pure ice melts at 0 °C, and pure water boils at 100 °C). If a substance is impure, the melting point will be too low and the boiling point will be too high (so if some ice melts at –2 °C, it's probably got an impurity in it e.g. salt).

I wish they'd find a drug to cure exams...

£900 million. You could buy yourself an island. And one for your mum. And a couple for your mates...

Allotropes of Carbon

Allotropes are just different structural forms of the same element in the same physical state, e.g. they're all solids. Carbon has quite a few allotropes, and you get to learn all about them. You lucky thing.

Diamond is Used in Jewellery and Cutting Tools

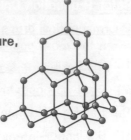

1) Diamonds are lustrous (sparkly) and colourless. Ideal for jewellery.

2) Each carbon atom forms four covalent bonds in a very rigid giant covalent structure, which makes diamond really hard. This makes diamonds ideal as cutting tools.

3) All those strong covalent bonds take a lot of energy to break and give diamond a very high melting point. Its high melting point is another reason diamond is so useful as a cutting tool.

4) It doesn't conduct electricity because it has no free electrons or ions.

Graphite Makes the Lead of Your Pencil

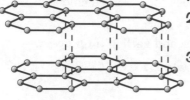

1) Graphite is black and opaque, but still kind of shiny.

2) Each carbon atom only forms three covalent bonds, creating sheets of carbon atoms which are free to slide over each other.

3) The layers are held together weakly so they are slippery and can be rubbed off onto paper to leave a black mark — that's how a pencil works. This also makes graphite ideal as a lubricating material.

4) Graphite's got a high melting point — the covalent bonds need loads of energy to break.

5) Since only three out of each carbon's four outer electrons are used in bonds, there are lots of delocalised (spare) electrons that can move. This means graphite conducts electricity.

Diamond and Graphite are Giant Molecular Structures

1) Because carbon can form lots of covalent bonds with itself, it can form giant molecular structures like diamond and graphite sheets.

2) Because of all the covalent bonds, giant molecular structures are strong, have high melting points and don't dissolve in water.

3) Giant molecular structures usually don't conduct electricity because there aren't any free electrons or ions — graphite is an exception to this.

Fullerenes are Nanoparticles

Nanoparticles are only a few nanometres (nm) across (1 nm = 0.000 000 001 m).

1) Fullerenes are molecules of carbon, shaped like closed tubes or hollow balls.

2) Fullerenes can be used to 'cage' other molecules. The fullerene structure forms around another atom or molecule, which is then trapped inside. This could be a new way of delivering a drug into the body, e.g. for slow release.

3) Fullerenes can be joined together to form nanotubes — tiny hollow carbon tubes.

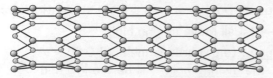

Nanotubes have a huge surface area, so they could help make great industrial catalysts — individual catalyst molecules could be attached to the nanotubes (the bigger the surface area the better).

Carbon is a girl's best friend...

Nanoparticles. Confused? Just think of it as knitting teeny weeny atomic footballs, and you'll be fine...

Revision Summary for Module C3

Some more tricky questions to stress you out. The thing is though, why bother doing easy questions? These meaty monsters find out what you really know, and worse, what you really don't. Yeah, I know, it's kinda scary, but if you want to get anywhere in life you've got to face up to a bit of hardship. That's just the way it is. Take a few deep breaths and then try these.

1) Give an example of: a) an endothermic reaction, b) an exothermic reaction.

2) Is bond breaking an exothermic or an endothermic reaction?

3) Give the formula that you would use to find the amount of energy transferred to the water in a calorimetric experiment.

4) Give three things you should do in order to make sure a calorimetric experiment is as accurate as possible.

5) How might you measure the rate of the reaction between calcium carbonate and hydrochloric acid?

6) Explain how increasing the collision frequency affects the rate of a chemical reaction.

7) What four things affect the rate of a reaction?

8) Why do gases react faster when they're under higher pressure?

9) Why do fine combustible powders sometimes explode?

10)* A piece of magnesium is added to a dilute solution of hydrochloric acid, and hydrogen gas is produced. The experiment is repeated with a more concentrated hydrochloric acid. How can you tell from the experiment which concentration of acid produces a faster rate of reaction?

11)* Find A_r or M_r for each of these (use the periodic table inside the front cover):
a) Ca b) Ag c) CO_2 d) $MgCO_3$ e) $Al(OH)_3$
f) ZnO g) Na_2CO_3 h) sodium chloride

12)* Write down the three steps of the method for calculating reacting masses.
a) What mass of magnesium oxide is produced when 112.1 g of magnesium burns in air?
b) What mass of sodium is needed to produce 108.2 g of sodium oxide (Na_2O)?
c) What mass of carbon will react with hydrogen to produce 24.6 g of propane (C_3H_8)?

13) Write the equation for calculating the atom economy of a reaction.

14) Explain why it is important to use industrial reactions with a high atom economy.

15) What is the formula for percentage yield? How does percentage yield differ from actual yield?

16) Name four factors that prevent the percentage yield being 100%

17) What are 'batch production' and 'continuous production'?

18) Explain the advantages of using batch production to make pharmaceutical drugs. What are the disadvantages?

19) It can take 12 years and about £900 million to bring a new drug to market. Explain why.

20) In terms of intermolecular bonds, explain why diamond makes a good cutting tool.

21) Why does graphite conduct electricity?

22) Do giant molecular structures have low or high melting points?

23) How might fullerenes be used to deliver drugs to the body?

* Answers on page 108.

The History of the Atom

If you cut up a cake you end up with slices. If you keep going you're gonna have crumbs. But what happens if you keep cutting... Just how small can you go and what would the stuff you end up with look like... Scientists have been trying to work it out for years...

The Theory of Atomic Structure Has Changed Throughout History

Atoms are the tiny particles of matter (stuff that has a mass) which make up everything in the universe...

1) At the start of the 19th century John Dalton described atoms as solid spheres, and said that different spheres made up the different elements.

2) In 1897 J J Thomson concluded from his experiments that atoms weren't solid spheres. His measurements of charge and mass showed that an atom must contain even smaller, negatively charged particles — electrons. The 'solid sphere' idea of atomic structure had to be changed. The new theory was known as the 'plum pudding model'.

delicious pudding

positively charged 'pudding'

electrons

Rutherford Showed that the Plum Pudding Model Was Wrong

1) In 1909 Ernest Rutherford and his students Hans Geiger and Ernest Marsden conducted the famous gold foil experiment. They fired positively charged particles at an extremely thin sheet of gold.

2) From the plum pudding model, they were expecting most of the particles to be deflected by the positive 'pudding' that made up most of an atom. In fact, most of the particles passed straight through the gold atoms, and a very small number were deflected backwards. So the plum pudding model couldn't be right.

3) So Rutherford came up with an idea that could explain this new evidence — the theory of the nuclear atom. In this, there's a tiny, positively charged nucleus at the centre, surrounded by a 'cloud' of negative electrons — most of the atom is empty space.

A few particles are deflected backwards by the nucleus.

Most of the particles pass through empty space.

The Refined Bohr Model Explains a Lot...

1) Scientists realised that electrons in a 'cloud' around the nucleus of an atom, as Rutherford described, would be attracted to the nucleus, causing the atom to collapse. Niels Bohr proposed a new model of the atom where all the electrons were contained in shells.

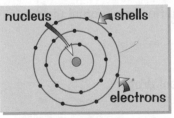

nucleus — shells
electrons

2) Bohr suggested that electrons can only exist in fixed orbits, or shells, and not anywhere in between. Each shell has a fixed energy.

3) Bohr's theory of atomic structure was supported by many experiments and it helped to explain lots of other scientists' observations at the time. It was pretty close to our currently accepted version of the atom (have a look at the next page to see what we now think atoms look like).

Scientific Theories Have to be Backed Up by Evidence

1) So, you can see that what we think the atom looks like now is completely different to what people thought in the past. These different ideas were accepted because they fitted the evidence available at the time.

2) As scientists did more experiments, new evidence was found and our theory of the structure of the atom was modified to fit it.

3) This is nearly always the way scientific knowledge develops — new evidence prompts people to come up with new, improved ideas. These ideas can be used to make predictions which if proved correct are a pretty good indication that the ideas are right.

4) Scientists also put their ideas and research up for peer review. This means everyone gets a chance to see the new ideas, check for errors and then other scientists can use it to help develop their own work.

I love a good model — Kate Moss is my favourite...

Scientists love a good theory but what they love more is trying to disprove their mate's one. That's how science works.

Atoms

There are quite a few <u>different</u> (and equally useful) <u>modern</u> models of the atom — but chemists tend to like this model best. You can use it to explain pretty much the whole of chemistry... which is nice.

The Nucleus

1) It's in the <u>middle</u> of the atom.

2) It contains <u>protons</u> and <u>neutrons</u>.

3) It has a <u>positive charge</u> because of the protons.

4) Almost the <u>whole</u> mass of the atom (about 10^{-23} g) is <u>concentrated</u> in the nucleus.

The Electrons

1) Move <u>around</u> the nucleus in electron <u>shells</u>.

2) They're <u>negatively charged</u>.

3) They're <u>tiny</u>, but they cover <u>a lot of space</u>.

4) The <u>volume</u> of their orbits determines the size of the atom — atoms have a radius of about 10^{-10} m.

5) Electrons have virtually <u>no</u> mass.

~ Atoms are really tiny, don't forget. ~
~ They're too small to see, even with ~
~ a very high power microscope. ~

- <u>Protons</u> are <u>heavy</u> and <u>positively charged</u>
- <u>Neutrons</u> are <u>heavy</u> and <u>neutral</u>
- <u>Electrons</u> are <u>tiny</u> and <u>negatively charged</u>

PARTICLE	MASS	CHARGE
Proton	1	+1
Neutron	1	0
Electron	0.0005	−1

(<u>Electron mass</u> is often taken as <u>zero</u>.)

Number of Protons Equals Number of Electrons

1) Neutral atoms have <u>no charge</u> overall (unlike ions, see page 63).

2) This is because they have the <u>same number</u> of <u>protons</u> as <u>electrons</u>.

3) The <u>charge</u> on the electrons is the <u>same</u> size as the charge on the <u>protons</u>, but <u>opposite</u> — so the charges <u>cancel out</u>.

Atomic Number and Mass Number Describe an Atom

These two numbers tell you how many of each kind of particle an atom has.

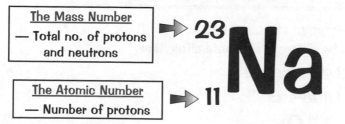

The Mass Number
— Total no. of protons and neutrons

The Atomic Number
— Number of protons

$^{23}_{11}$**Na**

1) The <u>atomic (proton) number</u> tells you how many <u>protons</u> there are.

2) Atoms of the <u>same</u> element all have the <u>same</u> number of <u>protons</u> — so atoms of <u>different</u> elements will have <u>different</u> numbers of protons.

3) To get the number of <u>neutrons</u>, just subtract the <u>atomic number</u> from the <u>mass number</u>.

4) The <u>mass (nucleon) number</u> is always the <u>biggest</u> number. On a periodic table the mass number is actually the <u>relative atomic mass</u> (see page 51).

Number of protons = number of electrons...

This stuff might seem a bit useless at first, but it should be permanently engraved into your mind. If you don't know these basic facts, you've got no chance of understanding the rest of chemistry. So <u>learn it now</u>, and watch as the Universe unfolds and reveals its timeless mysteries to you...

Elements and Isotopes

Elements are substances made up of only <u>one type</u> of atom, e.g. carbon is made up of <u>just</u> carbon atoms.

The Periodic Table is a Table of All Known Elements

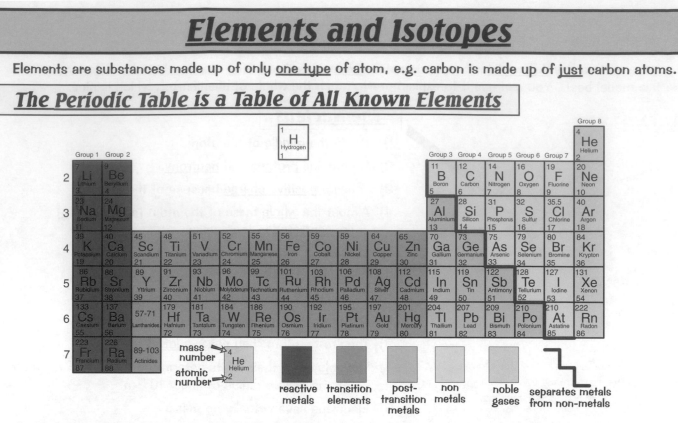

1) There are 100ish elements, which all materials are made of. More are still being 'discovered'.

2) The <u>modern</u> periodic table shows the elements in order of ascending <u>atomic number</u>.

3) The periodic table is laid out so that elements with <u>similar properties</u> form <u>columns</u>.

4) These <u>vertical columns</u> are called <u>groups</u> and roman numerals are often (but not always) used for them.

5) The <u>group</u> to which the element belongs <u>corresponds</u> to the <u>number of electrons</u> it has in its <u>outer shell</u>. E.g. <u>Group 1</u> elements have <u>1</u> outer shell electron, <u>Group 7</u> elements have <u>7</u> outer shell electrons and so on. <u>Group 8</u> elements have <u>8</u> electrons in their outer shell — this means their outer shell is <u>full</u>.

6) The rows are called <u>periods</u>. Each new period represents another full <u>shell</u> of electrons (see page 62).

7) The period to which the element belongs corresponds to the <u>number of shells</u> of electrons it has.

Isotopes are the Same Except for an Extra Neutron or Two

> <u>Isotopes</u> are different forms of the same element, which have the <u>same number of protons</u> but a <u>different number of neutrons</u>.

1) Isotopes have the <u>same atomic number</u> but <u>different mass numbers</u>.

2) <u>If</u> they had <u>different</u> atomic numbers, they'd be <u>different</u> elements altogether.

3) A very popular pair of isotopes are <u>carbon-12</u> and <u>carbon-14</u>.

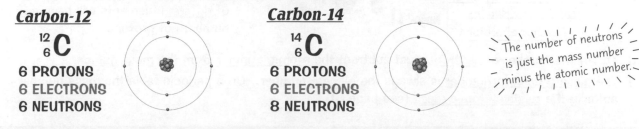

Carbon-12

$^{12}_{6}C$

6 PROTONS
6 ELECTRONS
6 NEUTRONS

Carbon-14

$^{14}_{6}C$

6 PROTONS
6 ELECTRONS
8 NEUTRONS

The number of neutrons is just the mass number minus the atomic number.

This table comes up periodically...

Scientists are still producing <u>new</u> elements in particle accelerators, but they're all <u>radioactive</u>.
Most only last a fraction of a second before they decay — they're up to element 118 at the moment.

History of the Periodic Table

We haven't always known as much about Chemistry as we do now. No sirree. Take the periodic table. Early chemists looked to try and understand patterns in the elements' properties to get a bit of understanding.

Döbereiner Tried to Organise Elements into Triads

Back in the 1800's the only thing they could measure was relative atomic mass, and so the known elements were arranged in order of atomic mass.

In 1828 a guy called Döbereiner started to put this list of elements into groups based on their chemical properties. He put the elements into groups of three, which he called triads. E.g. Cl, Br and I were one triad, and Li, Na and K were another.

The middle element of each triad had a relative atomic mass that was the average of the other two.

Element	Relative atomic mass
Lithium	7
Sodium	23
Potassium	39

$(7 + 39) \div 2 = 23$

Newlands' Law of Octaves Was the First Good Effort

A chap called Newlands had the first good stab at arranging things more usefully in 1864. He noticed that every eighth element had similar properties, and so he listed some of the known elements in rows of seven:

H	Li	Be	B	C	N	O
F	Na	Mg	Al	Si	P	S
Cl	K	Ca	Cr	Ti	Mn	Fe

These sets of eight were called Newlands' Octaves. Unfortunately the pattern broke down on the third row, with transition metals like titanium (Ti) and iron (Fe) messing it up.

It was because he left no gaps that his work was ignored. But he was getting pretty close, as you can see.

Newlands presented his ideas to the Chemical Society in 1865. But his work was criticised because:

1) His groups contained elements that didn't have similar properties, e.g. carbon and titanium.

2) He mixed up metals and non-metals e.g. oxygen and iron.

3) He didn't leave any gaps for elements that hadn't been discovered yet.

Dmitri Mendeleev Left Gaps and Predicted New Elements

1) In 1869, Dmitri Mendeleev in Russia, armed with about 50 known elements, arranged them into his Table of Elements — with various gaps as shown.

2) Mendeleev put the elements in order of atomic mass (like Newlands did). But Mendeleev found he had to leave gaps in order to keep elements with similar properties in the same vertical groups — and he was prepared to leave some very big gaps in the first two rows before the transition metals come in on the third row.

Mendeleev's Table of the Elements

```
H
Li Be                                      B  C  N  O  F
Na Mg                                      Al Si P  S  Cl
K  Ca *  Ti V  Cr Mn Fe Co Ni Cu Zn *  *  As Se Br
Rb Sr Y  Zr Nb Mo *  Ru Rh Pd Ag Cd In Sn Sb Te I
Cs Ba *  *  Ta W  *  Os Ir Pt Au Hg Tl Pb Bi
```

3) The gaps were the really clever bit because they predicted the properties of so far undiscovered elements. When they were found and they fitted the pattern it was pretty smashing news for old Dmitri. The rogue.

4) Mendeleev's table made even more sense when later discoveries on atomic structure were made:

- each element has an atomic number exactly one more than the previous element (see page 60).

- the pattern in the periodic table — two elements in the first row, eight in the second and eight in the third, matches the way electrons are arranged in an atom — two in a first shell, eight in a second and eight in a third. There's more about this on the next page.

Julie Andrews' octaves — do-re-mi-fa-so-la-ti-do...

This is a good example of how science often progresses — even now. A scientist has a basically good (though incomplete) idea. Other scientists laugh and mock and generally deride. Eventually, the idea is modified a bit to take account of the available evidence, and voilà — into the textbooks it goes.

Electron Shells

Electron shells... orbits electrons zoom about in.

Electron Shell Rules:

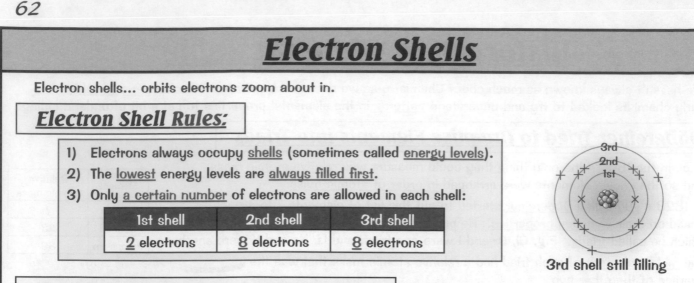

1) Electrons always occupy <u>shells</u> (sometimes called <u>energy levels</u>).
2) The <u>lowest</u> energy levels are <u>always filled first</u>.
3) Only <u>a certain number</u> of electrons are allowed in each shell:

1st shell	2nd shell	3rd shell
<u>2</u> electrons	<u>8</u> electrons	<u>8</u> electrons

3rd shell still filling

Working Out Electron Configurations

You need to know the <u>electron configurations</u> for the first <u>20</u> elements. They're shown in the diagram below — but they're not hard to work out. For a quick example, take nitrogen. <u>Follow the steps</u>...

1) The periodic table tells you that nitrogen has <u>seven</u> protons... so it must have <u>seven</u> electrons.
2) Follow the '<u>Electron Shell Rules</u>' above. The <u>first</u> shell can only take 2 electrons and the <u>second</u> shell can take a <u>maximum</u> of 8 electrons.
3) So the electron configuration for nitrogen must be 2,5 — easy peasy. Now you try it for argon.

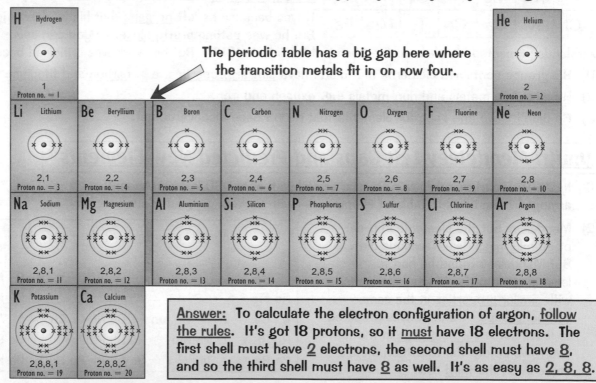

The periodic table has a big gap here where the transition metals fit in on row four.

<u>Answer:</u> To calculate the electron configuration of argon, <u>follow the rules</u>. It's got 18 protons, so it <u>must</u> have 18 electrons. The first shell must have <u>2</u> electrons, the second shell must have <u>8</u>, and so the third shell must have <u>8</u> as well. It's as easy as <u>2, 8, 8</u>.

You can use the electronic configuration to work out the <u>period</u>, <u>group</u> and <u>atomic number</u> of an element.

- The period of the element is the same as the <u>number of shells</u> which contain electrons.
- The group number can be found by looking at <u>how many electrons</u> occupy the <u>outer shell</u> of the element.
  <u>Example</u>: Sodium has the electronic configuration <u>2,8,1</u>. The <u>period</u> number is <u>3</u> as there are 3 shells occupied. The <u>group</u> number is <u>1</u> as there is 1 electron in the outer shell.
- The atomic number is found by <u>adding up</u> all the electrons. You can use it to <u>identify</u> elements. E.g. an electronic configuration of <u>2,8,2</u> gives an atomic number of <u>12</u>, which tells you the element is <u>Mg</u>.

One little duck and two fat ladies — 2, 8, 8...

You need to know enough about electron shells to draw out that <u>whole diagram</u> at the bottom of the page without looking at it. Obviously, you don't have to learn each element separately, just <u>learn the pattern</u>.

Ionic Bonding

An ion is an atom or molecule which has lost or gained electrons to become <u>charged</u>.

Ionic Bonding — Transferring Electrons

In <u>ionic bonding</u>, atoms <u>lose or gain electrons</u> to form <u>charged particles</u> (or <u>ions</u>) which are then <u>strongly attracted</u> to one another (because of the attraction of opposite charges, + and –).

A Shell with Just One Electron is Well Keen to Get Rid...

1) All the atoms over at the <u>left-hand side</u> of the periodic table, such as sodium, magnesium etc., have just <u>one or two electrons</u> in their <u>outer shell</u>.

2) They're pretty keen to lose them, because then they'll only have <u>full shells</u> left, which is how they like it.

3) So given half a chance they do get rid, and that leaves the atom as a <u>positive ion</u> instead.

4) Ions are very reactive and will <u>leap</u> at the first passing ion with an <u>opposite charge</u> and stick to it like glue.

A Nearly Full Shell is Well Keen to Get That Extra Electron...

1) On the <u>other side</u> of the periodic table the elements in <u>Group 6</u> and <u>Group 7</u>, such as <u>oxygen</u> and <u>chlorine</u>, have outer shells which are <u>nearly full</u>.

2) They're obviously pretty keen to <u>gain</u> that <u>extra one or two electrons</u> to fill the shell up.

3) When they do they become <u>negative ions</u> and before you know it, <u>pop</u>, they've latched onto the atom (ion) that gave up the electron a moment earlier.

4) The reaction of sodium and chlorine is a <u>classic case</u>:

① The <u>sodium</u> atom <u>gives up</u> its <u>outer electron</u> and becomes an Na⁺ ion.

② The <u>chlorine</u> atom <u>picks up</u> the <u>spare electron</u> and becomes a Cl⁻ ion.

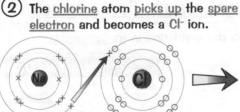 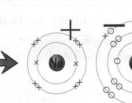

③ 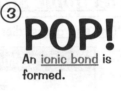 **POP!** An <u>ionic bond</u> is formed.

Ionic Compounds Form Giant Ionic Lattices

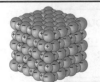

1) <u>Ionic bonds</u> form between <u>metals</u> and <u>non-metals</u> and always produce <u>giant ionic structures</u>.

2) The ions form a <u>closely packed</u> regular lattice arrangement. The ions are <u>not</u> free to move though, so these compounds do <u>not</u> conduct electricity when <u>solid</u>.

3) There are <u>very strong</u> chemical bonds between <u>all</u> the ions.

MgO and NaCl are Both Giant Ionic Structures

1) <u>Magnesium oxide</u> and <u>sodium chloride</u> both have high melting and boiling points. This is due to the <u>very strong</u> attraction between <u>oppositely charged ions</u> in the giant structures. To break the bonds you have to <u>overcome</u> these attractive forces — this takes a lot of energy.

2) MgO has a <u>higher melting point</u> than NaCl. It's made of Mg^{2+} and O^{2-} ions, which have <u>double the charge</u> of Na⁺ and Cl⁻ ions, so the <u>attraction</u> between them is <u>harder to overcome</u>. O^{2-} ions are also <u>smaller</u> than Cl⁻ ions, so the ions in MgO can <u>pack together more closely</u>. This <u>also</u> makes the <u>attraction</u> between them <u>harder to overcome</u>.

3) When MgO and NaCl <u>melt</u>, the ions are <u>free to move</u> and they'll conduct electricity.

Melted

Dissolved in Water

4) NaCl <u>dissolves</u> to form a solution that <u>conducts electricity</u>. When dissolved the ions <u>separate</u> and are all <u>free to move</u> in the solution, so they can carry <u>electric current</u>.

Giant ionic lattices — all over your chips...

Because they conduct electricity when they're dissolved in water, ionic compounds are used to make some types of <u>battery</u>. The solution used to leak all over the place but they can now make it into a <u>conductive paste</u>. Clever.

Ions and Ionic Compounds

Ions crop up all over the place in chemistry. You're gonna have to be able to work out formulas for compounds from their ions and draw some nifty diagrams to show it too. You'd better get on...

Simple Ions — Groups 1 & 2 and 6 & 7

1) Ions are charged particles — they can be single atoms (e.g. Cl^-) or groups of atoms (e.g. NO_3^-).

2) When atoms lose or gain electrons to form ions, all they're trying to do is get a full outer shell (also called a "stable electronic structure"). Atoms like full outer shells — it's atom heaven.

3) When metals form ions, they lose electrons to form positive ions.

4) When non-metals form ions, they gain electrons to form negative ions.

5) So when a metal and a non-metal combine, they form ionic bonds.

6) The number of electrons lost or gained is the same as the charge on the ion. E.g. If 2 electrons are lost the charge is 2^+. If 3 electrons are gained the charge is 3^-.

7) To work out the formula of an ionic compound, you have to balance the +ve and the –ve charges.

Potassium Chloride	Potassium oxide	Magnesium chloride
$K^+ + Cl^- \longrightarrow KCl$	$2K^+ + O^{2-} \longrightarrow K_2O$	$Mg^{2+} + 2Cl^- \longrightarrow MgCl_2$
The potassium ion is 1+, and the chloride ion is 1–, so they balance.	The potassium ion is 1+, and the oxygen ion is 2–, so you need two K^+ ions to balance the O^{2-} ion.	The magnesium ion is 2+, and the chloride ion is 1–, so you need two Cl^- ions to balance the Mg^{2+} ion.

Electronic Structure of Some Simple Ionic Compounds

'Dot and cross' diagrams show what happens to the electrons in ionic bonds:

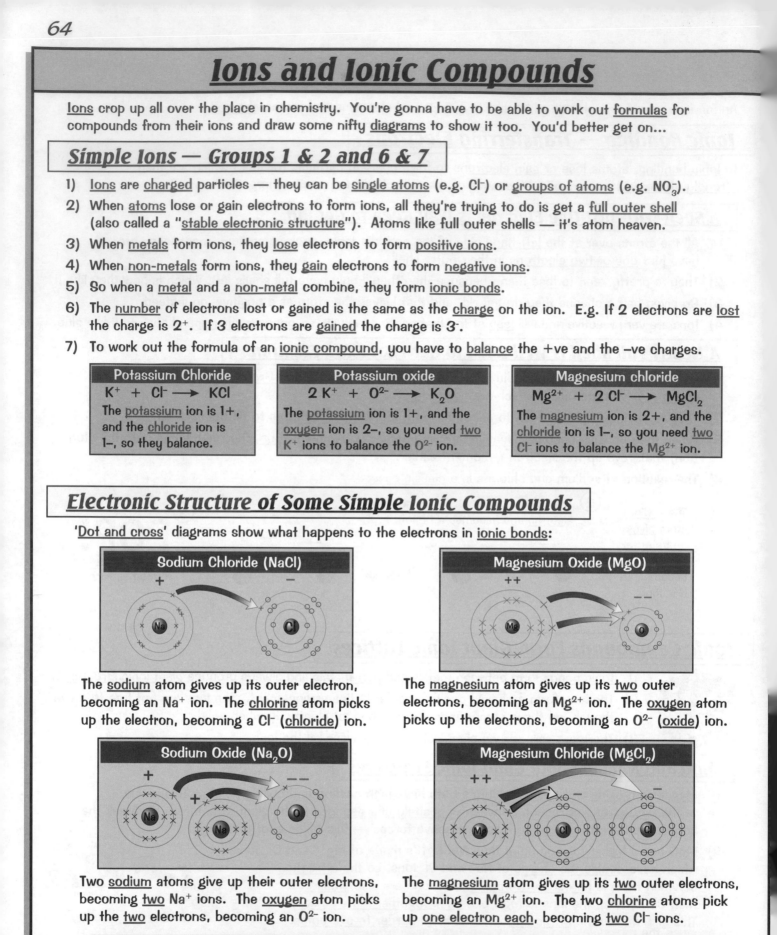

The sodium atom gives up its outer electron, becoming an Na^+ ion. The chlorine atom picks up the electron, becoming a Cl^- (chloride) ion.

The magnesium atom gives up its two outer electrons, becoming an Mg^{2+} ion. The oxygen atom picks up the electrons, becoming an O^{2-} (oxide) ion.

Two sodium atoms give up their outer electrons, becoming two Na^+ ions. The oxygen atom picks up the two electrons, becoming an O^{2-} ion.

The magnesium atom gives up its two outer electrons, becoming an Mg^{2+} ion. The two chlorine atoms pick up one electron each, becoming two Cl^- ions.

Notice that all the atoms end up with full outer shells as a result of this giving and taking of electrons.

Full Shells — it's the name of the game...

Here's where you can get a little practice working out formulas for molecules. Remember to balance them, or you'll lose marks. Some elements like to gain electrons, some like to lose electrons, but they all want to have a full outer shell. Poor little electron shells, all they want in life is to be full...

Covalent Bonding

But wait — ionic bonding isn't the only way atoms can join together. Atoms can also <u>share</u> electrons to create very strong covalent bonds. Ah... aint that nice.

Covalent Bonds — Sharing Electrons

1) When <u>non-metal atoms</u> combine together they form <u>covalent bonds</u> by <u>sharing</u> pairs of electrons.

2) This way <u>both atoms</u> feel that they have <u>a full outer shell</u>, and that makes them happy.

3) <u>Each</u> covalent bond provides <u>one extra</u> shared electron for each atom.

4) Each atom involved has to make <u>enough</u> covalent bonds to <u>fill up</u> its outer shell.

5) <u>Learn</u> these important examples:

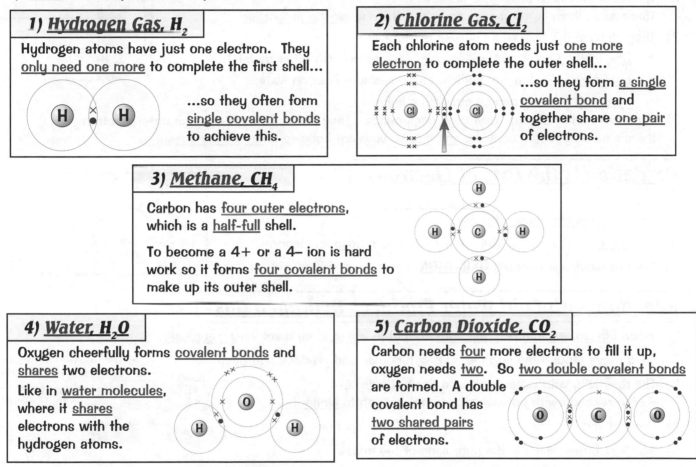

1) Hydrogen Gas, H_2

Hydrogen atoms have just one electron. They <u>only need one more</u> to complete the first shell...

...so they often form <u>single covalent bonds</u> to achieve this.

2) Chlorine Gas, Cl_2

Each chlorine atom needs just <u>one more</u> <u>electron</u> to complete the outer shell...

...so they form <u>a single</u> <u>covalent bond</u> and together share <u>one pair</u> of electrons.

3) Methane, CH_4

Carbon has <u>four outer electrons</u>, which is a <u>half-full</u> shell.

To become a 4+ or a 4– ion is hard work so it forms <u>four covalent bonds</u> to make up its outer shell.

4) Water, H_2O

Oxygen cheerfully forms <u>covalent bonds</u> and <u>shares</u> two electrons.

Like in <u>water molecules</u>, where it <u>shares</u> electrons with the hydrogen atoms.

5) Carbon Dioxide, CO_2

Carbon needs <u>four</u> more electrons to fill it up, oxygen needs <u>two</u>. So <u>two double covalent bonds</u> are formed. A double covalent bond has <u>two shared pairs</u> of electrons.

Simple Molecular Substances

1) Substances formed from <u>covalent bonds</u> usually have <u>simple molecular structures</u>, like CO_2 and H_2O.

2) The atoms within the molecules are held together by <u>very strong covalent bonds</u>.

3) By contrast, the forces of attraction <u>between</u> these molecules are <u>very weak</u>.

4) The <u>result</u> of these <u>feeble intermolecular forces</u> is that the melting and boiling points are <u>very low</u>, because the molecules are <u>easily parted</u> from each other.

5) Most molecular substances are <u>gases or liquids</u> at room temperature.

6) Molecular substances <u>don't conduct electricity</u>, simply because there are <u>no free electrons</u> or ions.

weak intermolecular forces

Carbon dioxide   Water

It's good to share — especially when it's somebody else's...

If a compound has a <u>simple molecular structure</u>, you need to be able to predict its properties. So remember — <u>low</u> melting and boiling points, so probably a <u>gas</u> or <u>liquid</u> at room temperature, and <u>doesn't conduct electricity</u>.

Group 1 — Alkali Metals

Welcome to the wonderful world of the <u>alkali metals</u>. May I introduce Li, Na, K, Rb, Cs and Fr...

Group 1 Metals are Known as the 'Alkali Metals'

Group 1 metals include lithium, sodium and potassium... know those three names real well. They could also ask you about rubidium and caesium.

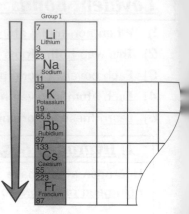

As you go <u>DOWN</u> Group 1, the alkali metals become <u>more reactive</u> — the <u>outer electron</u> is more easily <u>lost</u>, because it's further from the nucleus (the <u>atomic radius</u> is <u>larger</u>) so <u>less energy</u> is needed to remove it.

1) The alkali metals all have <u>ONE outer electron</u>.
   This makes them <u>very reactive</u> and gives them all <u>similar properties</u>.

2) They all have the following <u>physical properties</u>:
   • <u>Low melting point</u> and <u>boiling point</u> (compared with other metals).
   • <u>Low density</u> — lithium, sodium and potassium float on water.
   • <u>Very soft</u> — they can be cut with a knife.

3) The alkali metals always form <u>ionic</u> compounds. They are so keen to lose the outer electron there's no way they'd consider <u>sharing</u>, so covalent bonding is <u>out of the question</u>.

Oxidation is the Loss of Electrons

1) Group 1 metals are keen to <u>lose an electron</u> to form a <u>1⁺ ion</u> with a <u>stable electronic structure</u>.

2) The <u>more</u> reactive the metal the happier it is to <u>lose</u> an electron.

3) Loss of electrons is called <u>OXIDATION</u>.

$$Li - e^- \rightarrow Li^+$$

Reaction with Cold Water Produces Hydrogen Gas

1) When <u>lithium</u>, <u>sodium</u> or <u>potassium</u> are put in <u>water</u>, they react very <u>vigorously</u>.

2) They <u>move</u> around the surface, <u>fizzing</u> furiously and produce <u>hydrogen</u>.

3) The reactivity with water increases down the group
   — the reaction with potassium gets hot enough to <u>ignite</u> it.

4) Sodium and potassium <u>melt</u> in the heat of the reaction.

5) An <u>alkali</u> forms which is the <u>hydroxide</u> of the metal.

A lighted splint will <u>indicate</u> hydrogen by producing the notorious "<u>squeaky pop</u>" as the H_2 ignites.

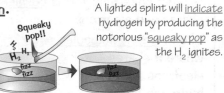

2Na	+	2H$_2$O	→	2NaOH	+	H$_2$
Sodium	+	Water	→	Sodium hydroxide	+	Hydrogen

Rubidium and caesium are even more reactive than potassium. This means they react more violently with water. They even explode when they get wet...

6) This happens with <u>all</u> the alkali metals (lithium forms LiOH, potassium forms KOH etc.). For the exam you could be asked about <u>any</u> of them so make sure you can write <u>balanced equations</u> for each one.

Alkali Metal Compounds Burn with Characteristic Colours

1) Dip a wire loop into some <u>hydrochloric acid</u> to clean and moisten it.

2) Put the loop into a <u>powdered</u> sample of the compound to be tested, then place the end in a <u>blue Bunsen flame</u>.

3) Alkali metal ions will give pretty coloured flames — the colour of the flame tells you which <u>alkali metal</u> is present.

Lithium:	<u>Red</u> flame
Sodium:	<u>Yellow/orange</u> flame
Potassium:	Lilac flame

Red and orange and pink and green — or something like that...

Alkali metals are <u>really reactive</u>. They're so reactive in fact they have to be stored in oil — otherwise they just react with the air. Learn the <u>trends</u> and <u>characteristics</u> of alkali metals before turning over.

Group 7 — Halogens

Here's a page on another periodic group — the halogens...

Group 7 Elements are Known as the 'Halogens'

1) Group 7 is made up of fluorine, chlorine, bromine, iodine and astatine.
2) All Group 7 elements have <u>7 electrons in their outer shell</u> — so they all react by <u>gaining one electron</u> to form a negative ion.
3) This means they've all got <u>similar properties</u>.

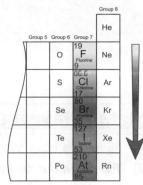

> As you go <u>DOWN</u> Group 7, the halogens become <u>less reactive</u> — there's less inclination to gain the <u>extra electron</u> to fill the outer shell when it's <u>further out</u> from the nucleus (there's a <u>larger atomic radius</u>).

4) As you go <u>down group 7</u> the <u>melting points</u> and <u>boiling points</u> of the halogens <u>increase</u>.
5) This means that at <u>room temperature</u>:

- <u>Chlorine</u> (Cl_2) is a fairly reactive, poisonous, <u>dense green gas</u> (low boiling point).
- <u>Bromine</u> (Br_2) is a dense, poisonous, <u>orange liquid</u>.
- <u>Iodine</u> (I_2) is a <u>dark grey crystalline solid</u> (high boiling point).

Reduction is the Gain of Electrons

1) Halogens are keen to <u>gain an electron</u> to form a <u>1⁻ ion</u> with a <u>stable electronic structure</u>.
2) The <u>more</u> reactive the halogen the happier it is to <u>gain</u> an electron.
3) Gain of electrons is called <u>REDUCTION</u>.

$$Cl_2 + 2e^- \rightarrow 2Cl^-$$

Halogen molecule   Halide ion

The Halogens React with Alkali Metals to Form Salts

The Halogens react vigorously with alkali metals (group 1 elements, see page 66) to form <u>salts</u> called '<u>metal halides</u>'.

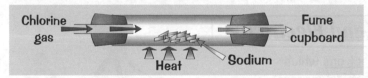

Chlorine gas   Fume cupboard   Heat   Sodium

Make sure you can write equations for the reactions between <u>all</u> the group 1 and group 7 elements.

$$2Na + Cl_2 \rightarrow 2NaCl$$
Sodium + Chlorine → Sodium chloride
$$2K + Br_2 \rightarrow 2KBr$$
Potassium + Bromine → Potassium bromide

More Reactive Halogens Will Displace Less Reactive Ones

<u>Chlorine</u> can displace <u>bromine</u> and <u>iodine</u> from a solution of <u>bromide</u> or <u>iodide</u>. <u>Bromine</u> will also displace <u>iodine</u>. You could be asked to <u>predict</u> the results of displacement reactions using <u>other halogens</u> — just remember, more reactive halogens displace less reactive ones.

Remember to balance the symbol equation properly or you'll lose marks in the exam.

Cl_2 gas

Solution of Potassium iodide

Iodine forming in solution

$$Cl_2 + 2KI \rightarrow I_2 + 2KCl$$
Chlorine + Potassium iodide → Iodine + Potassium chloride
$$Cl_2 + 2KBr \rightarrow Br_2 + 2KCl$$
Chlorine + Potassium bromide → Bromine + Potassium chloride

Halogens — one electron short of a full shell...

The halogens are another group from the periodic table, and just like the alkali metals (p.66) you've got to learn their trends and the equations on this page. <u>Learn</u> them, <u>cover</u> up the page, <u>scribble</u>, <u>check</u>.

Metals

Loads of elements are metals and they all have really <u>useful properties</u>. Make sure you learn 'em well.

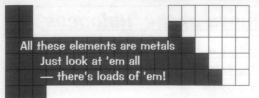

All these elements are metals
Just look at 'em all
— there's loads of 'em!

Metals Have a Crystal Structure

1) <u>All</u> metals have the <u>same</u> basic properties.
2) These are due to the <u>special type of bonding</u> that exists in metals.
3) Metals are held together with <u>metallic bonds</u>.
4) These special bonds allow the <u>outer electron(s)</u> of each atom to move freely.
5) This creates a '<u>sea</u>' of <u>delocalised</u> (free) <u>electrons</u> throughout the metal which is what gives rise to many of the properties of metals.

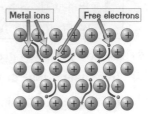

Metal ions   Free electrons

Most Have High Melting and Boiling Points, and High Density

1) Metals are very <u>hard</u>, <u>dense</u> and <u>lustrous</u> (i.e. shiny).
2) There's a <u>strong attraction</u> between the <u>delocalised electrons</u> and the closely packed <u>positive ions</u> — causing very <u>strong metallic bonding</u>.
3) Metals have <u>high melting</u> and <u>boiling points</u> because of these <u>strong metallic bonds</u>. You need to use a lot of <u>energy</u> to break them apart.
4) The <u>strength</u> of the metallic bond (and the <u>melting point</u>) <u>decreases</u> as <u>atomic radius increases</u>.

They're Strong, but Also Bendy and Malleable

1) Metals have a <u>high tensile strength</u> — in other words they're <u>strong</u> and <u>hard to break</u>.
2) But they can also be <u>hammered</u> into a different shape (they're malleable).

They're Good Conductors of Heat and Electricity

1) This is entirely due to the sea of <u>delocalised electrons</u> which move freely through the metal, carrying the <u>electrical current</u>.
2) They also carry the <u>heat energy</u> through the metal.

Don't try this at home. You'll die.

You've Got to be Able to Match the Metal to the Use

Use	Properties	Metal
Saucepans	Good conductor of heat, doesn't rust easily	Stainless Steel — and it's cheap too.
Electrical Wiring	Good conductor of electricity, easily bent	Copper. One of the best conductors around.
Aeroplanes	Low density (light), strong, doesn't corrode	Aluminium. Titanium's sometimes used, but it's a lot more expensive.
Bridges	Strong	Steel — this is mostly iron, but it's got a little bit of carbon in it, which makes it a lot less brittle.

In the exam you might have to suggest properties needed by a metal for a particular use.

Daniel Craig — he's definitely a strong Bond...

It's not just the main structure of an aeroplane that's made of aluminium — parts of the <u>engines</u>, the <u>seat supports</u> and even the cabin crew's <u>trolleys</u> are all made of aluminium. All this aluminium means the plane's light enough to fly.

Superconductors and Transition Metals

Oooooo, some interesting stuff...

At Very Low Temperatures, Some Metals are Superconductors

1) Normally, all metals have some electrical resistance — even really good conductors like copper.

2) That resistance means that whenever electricity flows through them, they heat up, and some of the electrical energy is wasted as heat.

3) If you make some metals cold enough, though, their resistance disappears completely. The metal becomes a superconductor.

4) Without any resistance, none of the electrical energy is turned into heat, so none of it's wasted.

5) That means you could start a current flowing through a superconducting circuit, take out the battery, and the current would carry on flowing forever.

So What's the Catch...

1) Using superconducting wires you can make:

   a) Power cables that transmit electricity without any loss of power (loss-free power transmission).

   b) Really strong electromagnets that don't need a constant power source.

   c) Electronic circuits that work really fast, because there's no resistance to slow them down.

2) But here's the catch — when I said cold, I meant REALLY COLD. Metals only start superconducting at less than –265 °C! Getting things that cold is very hard, and very expensive, which limits the use of superconductors.

3) Scientists are trying to develop room temperature superconductors now. So far, they've managed to get some weird metal oxide things to superconduct at about –135 °C, which is a much cheaper temperature to get down to. They've still got a long way to go though — ideally they need to develop superconductors that still work at 20 °C.

Metals in the Middle of the Periodic Table are Transition Metals

A lot of everyday metals are transition metals (e.g. copper, iron, zinc, gold, silver, platinum) — but there are loads of others as well. Transition metals have typical 'metallic' properties.

If you get asked about a transition metal you've never heard of — don't panic. These 'new' transition metals follow all the properties you've already learnt for the others. It's just that some folk get worried by the unfamiliar names.

These are the transition metals

| Sc | Ti | V | Cr | Mn | Fe | Co | Ni | Cu | Zn |

Transition Metals and Their Compounds Make Good Catalysts

1) Iron is the catalyst used in the Haber process for making ammonia.

2) Nickel is useful for the hydrogenation of alkenes (e.g. to make margarine).

The Compounds are Very Colourful

The compounds of transition elements are colourful due to the transition metal ion they contain. E.g. Iron(II) compounds are usually light green, iron(III) compounds are orange/brown (e.g. rust) and copper compounds are often blue.

Mendeleev and his amazing technicoloured periodic table...

Superconducting magnets are used in magnetic resonance image (MRI) scanners in hospitals. That way, the huge magnetic fields they need can be generated without using up a load of electricity. Great stuff...

Thermal Decomposition and Precipitation

There's an awful lot of stuff to learn on this page so you'd better get started...

1) Thermal Decomposition — Breaking Down with Heat

1) <u>Thermal decomposition</u> is when a substance <u>breaks down</u> into at least two other substances when <u>heated</u>.

2) <u>Transition metal carbonates</u> break down on heating. Transition metal carbonates are things like copper(II) carbonate ($CuCO_3$), iron(II) carbonate ($FeCO_3$), zinc carbonate ($ZnCO_3$) and manganese carbonate ($MnCO_3$), i.e. they've all got a <u>CO_3</u> bit in them.

3) They break down into a <u>metal oxide</u> (e.g. copper oxide, CuO) and <u>carbon dioxide</u>. This usually results in a <u>colour change</u>.

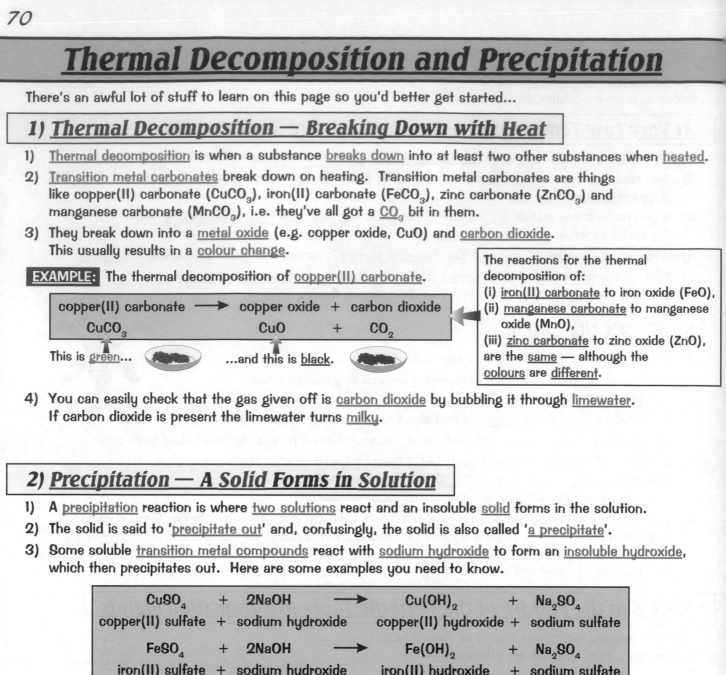

EXAMPLE: The thermal decomposition of <u>copper(II) carbonate</u>.

copper(II) carbonate $\longrightarrow$ copper oxide + carbon dioxide

$CuCO_3$ $\longrightarrow$ CuO + CO_2

This is <u>green</u>...   ...and this is <u>black</u>.

The reactions for the thermal decomposition of:
(i) <u>iron(II) carbonate</u> to iron oxide (FeO),
(ii) <u>manganese carbonate</u> to manganese oxide (MnO),
(iii) <u>zinc carbonate</u> to zinc oxide (ZnO),
are the <u>same</u> — although the <u>colours</u> are <u>different</u>.

4) You can easily check that the gas given off is <u>carbon dioxide</u> by bubbling it through <u>limewater</u>. If carbon dioxide is present the limewater turns <u>milky</u>.

2) Precipitation — A Solid Forms in Solution

1) A <u>precipitation</u> reaction is where <u>two solutions</u> react and an insoluble <u>solid</u> forms in the solution.

2) The solid is said to '<u>precipitate out</u>' and, confusingly, the solid is also called '<u>a precipitate</u>'.

3) Some soluble <u>transition metal compounds</u> react with <u>sodium hydroxide</u> to form an <u>insoluble hydroxide</u>, which then precipitates out. Here are some examples you need to know.

$$CuSO_4 + 2NaOH \longrightarrow Cu(OH)_2 + Na_2SO_4$$
copper(II) sulfate + sodium hydroxide   copper(II) hydroxide + sodium sulfate

$$FeSO_4 + 2NaOH \longrightarrow Fe(OH)_2 + Na_2SO_4$$
iron(II) sulfate + sodium hydroxide   iron(II) hydroxide + sodium sulfate

$$Fe_2(SO_4)_3 + 6NaOH \longrightarrow 2Fe(OH)_3 + 3Na_2SO_4$$
iron(III) sulfate + sodium hydroxide   iron(III) hydroxide + sodium sulfate

4) You can also write the above equations in terms of <u>ions</u>, for example:

$$Cu^{2+} + 2OH^- \longrightarrow Cu(OH)_2$$

Use Precipitation to Test for Transition Metal Ions

1) Some insoluble <u>transition metal hydroxides</u> have distinctive <u>colours</u>.

2) You can use this fact to <u>test</u> which transition metal ions a solution contains.

Copper(II) hydroxide is a blue solid.
Iron(II) hydroxide is a grey/green solid.
Iron(III) hydroxide is an orange/brown solid.

3) For example, if you add sodium hydroxide to an <u>unknown soluble salt</u>, and an <u>orange/brown</u> precipitate forms, you know you've got iron(III) hydroxide and so have <u>Fe^{3+}</u> ions in the solution.

My duffel coat's worn out — thermal decomposition...

Wow. This page is packed full of chemistry. I'm afraid you're gonna have to learn all the equations for <u>thermal decomposition</u> and <u>precipitation</u> and the <u>colours of the precipitates</u> if you want to impress the examiner.

Module C4 — The Periodic Table

Water Purity

Water, water, everywhere... well, there is if you live in Cumbria.

There are a Variety of Limited Water Resources in the UK

1) As well as for drinking, we need water for loads of <u>domestic</u> uses (mainly washing things).

2) <u>Industrially</u>, water is important as a <u>cheap raw material</u>, a <u>coolant</u> (especially in power stations) and a <u>solvent</u>. Between half and two thirds of all the fresh water used in the UK goes into industry.

> In the UK, we get our water from:
>
> 1) <u>SURFACE WATER</u>: <u>lakes</u>, <u>rivers</u> and <u>reservoirs</u> (artificial lakes). In much of England and Wales, these sources start to run dry during the summer months.
>
> 2) <u>GROUNDWATER</u>: <u>aquifers</u> (rocks that trap water underground). In parts of the south-east where surface water is very limited, as much as 70% of the domestic water supply comes from groundwater.

All these resources are <u>limited</u>, depending on <u>annual rainfall</u>, and demand for water increases every year. Experts worry that, unless we limit our water use, by 2025 we might not have enough water to supply everybody's needs. So it's important to <u>conserve water</u>.

Water is Purified in Water Treatment Plants

How much purification the water needs depends on the source. <u>Groundwater</u> from aquifers is usually quite pure, but <u>surface water</u> needs a lot of treatment. The processes include:

1) <u>Filtration</u> — a wire mesh screens out large twigs etc., and then gravel and sand beds filter out any other solid bits.

2) <u>Sedimentation</u> — iron sulfate or aluminium sulfate is added to the water, which makes fine particles clump together and settle at the bottom.

3) <u>Chlorination</u> — chlorine gas is bubbled through to kill <u>harmful bacteria</u> and other <u>microbes</u>.

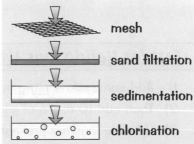

Some soluble impurities that are <u>dissolved</u> in the water are not removed — because they <u>can't</u> be <u>filtered</u> out. These include minerals which cause <u>water hardness</u> and some <u>harmful or poisonous chemicals</u> such as pesticides and fertilisers (see below).

Tap Water Can Still Contain Impurities

The water that comes out of our taps has to meet <u>strict safety standards</u>, but low levels of pollutants are still found. These pollutants come from various sources:

1) <u>Nitrate residues</u> from excess fertiliser 'run-off' into rivers and lakes. If too many nitrates get into drinking water it can cause serious health problems, especially for young babies. Nitrates prevent the blood from carrying oxygen properly.

2) <u>Lead compounds</u> from old lead pipes. Lead is very poisonous, particularly in children.

3) <u>Pesticide residues</u> from spraying too near to rivers and lakes.

You Can Get Fresh Water by Distilling Sea Water

1) In some very <u>dry</u> countries, e.g. Kuwait, sea water is <u>distilled</u> to produce drinking water.

2) Distillation needs <u>loads of energy</u>, so it's really <u>expensive</u> and not practical for producing large quantities of fresh water.

Who'd have thought there'd be so much to learn about water...

In the UK we're <u>very lucky</u> to have clean water available at the turn of a tap — but it's not a never-ending supply. <u>Learn</u> how water is purified in the UK, and what pollutants get through the cleaning process. <u>Cover</u>. <u>Scribble</u>.

Testing Water Purity

Here's another page on water and an interesting fact to keep you going... Taking a five-minute shower uses more water than a typical person in a slum in a developing country uses in a whole day. Crazy stuff.

You Can Test Water for Various Dissolved Ions

Water companies have to test their water regularly to make sure that pollutant levels don't exceed strict limits. You can test for some <u>dissolved ions</u> very easily using precipitation reactions (where two dissolved compounds react to form an insoluble solid — see page 70).

Test for Sulfate Ions Using Barium Chloride

1) Add some dilute <u>hydrochloric acid</u> to the test sample.
2) Then add 10 drops of <u>barium chloride solution</u>.
3) If you see a <u>white precipitate</u>, there are sulfate ions in the sample.

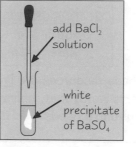

add $BaCl_2$ solution

white precipitate of $BaSO_4$

> barium ions + sulfate ions → barium sulfate
> Ba^{2+} + SO_4^{2-} → $BaSO_4$

4) Here's an example where potassium sulfate is present in the sample:

> barium chloride + potassium sulfate → barium sulfate + potassium chloride
> $BaCl_2$ + K_2SO_4 → $BaSO_4$ + KCl

Test for Halide Ions Using Silver Nitrate

1) Add some dilute <u>nitric acid</u> to the test sample.
2) Then add 10 drops of <u>silver nitrate solution</u>.
3) If halide ions are present a precipitate will form.

- <u>Chloride ions</u> will produce a <u>white precipitate</u>.
- <u>Bromide ions</u> will produce a <u>cream precipitate</u>.
- <u>Iodide ions</u> will produce a <u>pale yellow precipitate</u>.

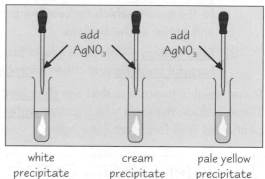

add $AgNO_3$ add $AgNO_3$

white precipitate of AgCl   cream precipitate of AgBr   pale yellow precipitate of AgI

4) These are the reactions you'll need to know for the exam:

> silver nitrate + sodium chloride → silver chloride + sodium nitrate
> $AgNO_3$ + $NaCl$ → $AgCl$ + $NaNO_3$

> silver nitrate + sodium bromide → silver bromide + sodium nitrate
> $AgNO_3$ + $NaBr$ → $AgBr$ + $NaNO_3$

> silver nitrate + sodium iodide → silver iodide + sodium nitrate
> $AgNO_3$ + NaI → AgI + $NaNO_3$

Two parts hydrogen, one part oxygen — hold the pollutants...

Water is amazingly important for us humans, but it's only <u>safe</u> to use if it's been tested properly for <u>pollutants</u>. One in eight people in the world don't have daily access to clean water and over two million people a year die from water related diseases. That's why it's so important for water companies to test their water <u>regularly</u>. Now, to brighten up your day, here comes a lovely revision summary. I know, I shouldn't have...

Revision Summary for Module C4

These certainly aren't the easiest questions you're going to come across. That's because they test what you know without giving you any clues. At first you might think they're impossibly difficult. Eventually you'll realise that they simply test whether you've learnt the stuff or not. If you're struggling to answer these then you need to do some serious learning.

1) Describe the famous 'gold foil experiment'. What did Rutherford conclude from it?
2) What are the three particles found in an atom? What are their relative masses and charges?
3) What do the mass number and atomic number represent?
4) What feature of atoms determines the order of the modern periodic table?
5) What are the periods and groups? Explain their significance in terms of electrons.
6) Explain what an isotope is. Give a well-known example.
7) Give two reasons why Newlands' Octaves were criticised.
8) Why did Mendeleev leave gaps in his Table of Elements?
9) List three facts (or 'rules') about electron shells.
10) Calculate the electron configuration for each of the following elements: ^4_2He, $^{12}_6C$, $^{31}_{15}P$, $^{39}_{19}K$.
11) Draw diagrams to show the electron arrangements for the first 20 elements.
12) What is ionic bonding?
13) Draw a diagram of a giant ionic lattice and give three features of giant ionic structures.
14) How many electrons are lost or gained for atoms to form 1+, 1−, 2+ and 2− ions?
15) Sketch dot and cross diagrams for: a) sodium chloride
                                      b) magnesium oxide
                                      c) sodium oxide
                                      d) magnesium chloride
16) What is covalent bonding?
17) Sketch dot and cross diagrams for: a) hydrogen gas
                                   b) water
                                   c) carbon dioxide
18) Describe the intermolecular forces between simple molecular substances.
19) Which group contains the alkali metals? How many electrons do they each have in their outer shell?
20) Give details of the reactions of the alkali metals with water.
21) Describe how you would determine whether a powdered sample contained sodium or potassium.
22) Describe the trend in reactivity of the halogens as you go down the group.
23) What is reduction?
24)* Write word equations and balanced symbol equations for the reactions between:
      a) bromine and lithium,   b) chlorine and potassium,   c) iodine and sodium.
25) Give details, with an equation, of a displacement reaction involving the halogens.
26) Give two properties of metals. Explain these properties in terms of the structure of a metal.
27) Why is copper used for electrical wiring?
28) What is a superconductor? Describe some useful applications of superconductors.
29) Name six transition metals, and give uses for two of them.
30) What are thermal decomposition reactions?
31) What type of reaction between two liquids results in the formation of a solid?
      What are these solid products called?
32) Describe a way to test solutions for transition metal ions.
33) Describe three processes used during the purification of surface water.
34) A student adds dilute hydrochloric acid and barium chloride to a water sample and a white precipitate is produced. What ions are present in the water?

* Answers on page 108

The Mole

The mole might seem a bit confusing. I think it's the word that puts people off. It's very difficult to see the relevance of the word "mole" to anything but a small burrowing animal. BUT... It's not actually that hard...

"THE MOLE" is Simply the Name Given to a Certain Number

Just like "a million" is this many: 1 000 000; or "a billion" is this many: 1 000 000 000, "a mole" is this many: 602 300 000 000 000 000 000 000   or 6.023×10^{23}.

Don't worry — you don't need to remember this number.

1) And that's all it is. Just a number. The burning question, of course, is why is it such a silly long one like that, and with a six at the front?

2) The answer is that when you get precisely that number of atoms or molecules, of any element or compound, then, conveniently, they weigh exactly the same number of grams as the relative atomic mass, A_r (or relative formula mass, M_r) of the element or compound. This is arranged on purpose of course, to make things easier.

Look back at page 51 if you've forgotten how to work out A_r and M_r.

> One mole of atoms or molecules of any substance will have a mass in grams equal to the relative formula mass (A_r or M_r) for that substance.

EXAMPLES:

Carbon has an A_r of 12.   So one mole of carbon weighs exactly 12 g

Nitrogen gas, N_2, has an M_r of 28 (2×14).   So one mole of N_2 weighs exactly 28 g

Carbon dioxide, CO_2, has an M_r of 44.   So one mole of CO_2 weighs exactly 44 g

Hexane, $CH_3(CH_2)_4CH_3$, has an M_r of 86 (12+3+((12+2)×4)+12+3). So one mole of pentane weighs exactly 86 g

This means that 12 g of carbon, or 28 g of N_2, or 44 g of CO_2, or 86 g of hexane all contain the same number of particles, namely one mole or 6.023×10^{23} atoms or molecules.

3) Molar mass is just another way of saying 'the mass of one mole'. Molar mass is measured in grams per mole. For example carbon has a molar mass of 12 g/mol.

Nice Easy Formula for Finding the Number of Moles in a Given Mass:

$$\text{NUMBER OF MOLES} = \frac{\text{Mass in g} \quad \text{(of element or compound)}}{M_r \quad \text{(of element or compound)}}$$

EXAMPLE 1: How many moles are there in 66 g of carbon dioxide?
M_r of CO_2 = 12 + (16 × 2) = 44
No. of moles = Mass (g) / M_r = 66/44 = 1.5 moles   Easy peasy.

This one's a tiny bit trickier. You have to rearrange the formula above.

EXAMPLE 2: What mass of carbon is there in 4 moles of carbon dioxide?
There are 4 moles of carbon in 4 moles of CO_2.
The mass of 4 moles of carbon = number of moles × M_r = 4 × 12 = 48 g

Relative Masses are Masses of Atoms Compared to Carbon-12

Atoms and molecules are much too tiny to weigh. So their masses are compared to 1/12th the mass of an atom of carbon-12. Carbon-12 is an isotope of carbon (see p60 for more on isotopes).

Learn this definition:

> The RELATIVE ATOMIC MASS of an element is the average mass of an atom of the element compared to the mass of $\frac{1}{12}$th of an atom of CARBON-12.

What do moles do for fun? Moller skate... *boom boom...*

Did you know that a mole can dig a tunnel at a rate of 18 feet per hour (that's really fast) and then move through an empty tunnel at 80 feet per hour. The word 'mole' can also mean a spy who infiltrates organisations and becomes a trusted member. And a small, brown skin lesion, otherwise known as melanocytic naevi. Great.

Reacting Masses and Empirical Formulas

You Can Use Moles to Calculate Masses in Reactions

You can work out the masses in a reaction using just <u>ratios</u> (see page 52) and by using <u>moles</u> too.

For example: Calculate the mass of aluminium oxide formed when 135 g of aluminium is burned in air.

1) Write out the <u>balanced equation</u>: $4Al + 3O_2 \rightarrow 2Al_2O_3$

2) <u>Calculate the number of moles</u> of aluminium in 135 g:

$$Moles = \frac{mass}{M_r} = \frac{135}{27} = 5$$

3) Look at the <u>ratio</u> of moles in the equation:

<u>4</u> moles of Al react to produce <u>2</u> moles of Al_2O_3 — <u>half</u> the number of moles are produced.
So <u>5</u> moles of Al will react to produce <u>2.5</u> moles of Al_2O_3

4) <u>Calculate the mass</u> of 2.5 moles of aluminium oxide: $mass = moles \times M_r = 2.5 \times 102 = 255\ g$

You Can Calculate the Percentage Composition by Mass of Compounds

For example, if you're told there are 42.9 g of potassium (K) in 61.6 g of potassium hydroxide (KOH) you could:

• use the <u>experimental data</u> to calculate the percentage composition of K in KOH: (42.9 ÷ 61.6) × 100 = <u>69.6%</u>.

• or use the <u>molecular formula</u>, <u>atomic masses</u> and the formula below...

$$\text{percentage composition by mass} = \frac{A_r \times \text{No. of atoms (of that element)}}{M_r \text{ (of whole compound)}} \times 100 = \frac{39 \times 1}{56} \times 100 = 69.6\%$$

Empirical Formulas are the Simplest Ratio of Atoms in a Compound

The <u>empirical formula</u> just gives the <u>smallest whole number ratio</u> of atoms in a compound.

For example: Ethane: chemical formula = C_2H_6 empirical formula = CH_3.
Glucose: chemical formula = $C_6H_{12}O_6$ empirical formula = CH_2O.

You have to be able to calculate an <u>empirical formula</u> from the <u>masses of each element</u> in a compound or the <u>percentage composition by mass</u> of each element in a sample of the compound.

It doesn't matter if you're given masses or percentages — you use the <u>same</u> easy <u>stepwise method</u>:

1) <u>List all the elements</u> in the compound (there are usually only two or three).

2) <u>Underneath them</u>, write their <u>experimental masses or percentages</u>.

3) <u>Divide</u> each mass or percentage <u>by the A_r</u> for that particular element.

4) Turn the numbers you get into <u>a simple ratio</u> by multiplying and/or dividing them by well-chosen numbers.

5) Get the ratio in its <u>simplest form</u>, and that tells you the empirical formula of the compound.

EXAMPLE: Find the empirical formula of the iron oxide produced when 44.8 g of iron reacts with 19.2 g of oxygen. (A_r for iron = 56, A_r for oxygen = 16)

METHOD:
1) List the two elements: Fe   O
2) Write in the experimental masses: 44.8   19.2
3) Divide by the A_r for each element: 44.8 ÷ 56 = 0.8   19.2 ÷ 16 = 1.2
4) Multiply by 10...   8   12
       ...then divide by 4   2   3
5) So the simplest formula is 2 atoms of Fe to 3 atoms of O, i.e. <u>Fe_2O_3</u>.

With this empirical formula I can rule the world! — mwa ha ha ha...

Now try these: 1) What is the <u>empirical formula</u> of: a) C_7H_{14}, b) $C_6H_{12}O_6$, c) Al_2Cl_6?

2) Find the <u>empirical formula</u> when 2.4 g of carbon react with 0.8 g of hydrogen.

Module C5 — How Much?

Concentration

Another dull and boring page. But at least there are some more calculations on it.

Concentration is a Measure of How Crowded Things Are

The concentration of a solution can be measured in moles per dm³ (i.e. moles per litre).
So 1 mole of stuff in 1 dm³ of solution has a concentration of 1 mole per dm³ (or 1 mol/dm³).

> The more solute you dissolve in a given volume, the more crowded the solute molecules are and the more concentrated the solution.

Concentration can also be measured in grams per dm³. So 56 grams of stuff dissolved in 1 dm³ of solution has a concentration of 56 grams per dm³.

There's a calculation you can do to convert moles per dm³ to grams per dm³ (see below). In the exam, look out for which one the question's asking for.

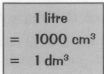

	1 litre
=	1000 cm³
=	1 dm³

Concentration = No. of Moles ÷ Volume

Here's a nice formula triangle for you to learn:

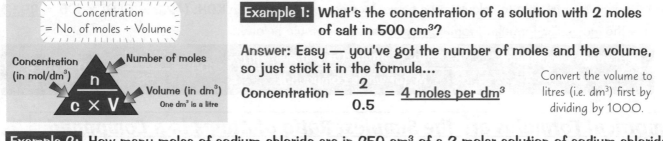

Concentration = No. of moles ÷ Volume

Concentration (in mol/dm³) — Number of moles

$$\frac{n}{c \times V}$$

Volume (in dm³) — One dm³ is a litre

Example 1: What's the concentration of a solution with 2 moles of salt in 500 cm³?

Answer: Easy — you've got the number of moles and the volume, so just stick it in the formula...

Concentration = $\frac{2}{0.5}$ = 4 moles per dm³

Convert the volume to litres (i.e. dm³) first by dividing by 1000.

Example 2: How many moles of sodium chloride are in 250 cm³ of a 3 molar solution of sodium chloride?

Answer: Well, 3 molar just means it's got 3 moles per dm³. So using the formula...
Number of moles = concentration × volume = 3 × 0.25 = 0.75 moles

3 molar is sometimes written '3 M'.

Converting Moles per dm³ to Grams per dm³

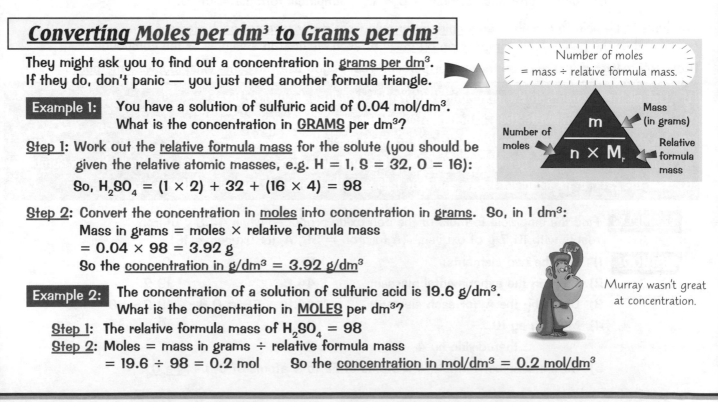

They might ask you to find out a concentration in grams per dm³. If they do, don't panic — you just need another formula triangle.

Number of moles = mass ÷ relative formula mass.

Number of moles — $\frac{m}{n \times M_r}$ — Mass (in grams), Relative formula mass

Example 1: You have a solution of sulfuric acid of 0.04 mol/dm³. What is the concentration in GRAMS per dm³?

Step 1: Work out the relative formula mass for the solute (you should be given the relative atomic masses, e.g. H = 1, S = 32, O = 16):
So, H_2SO_4 = (1 × 2) + 32 + (16 × 4) = 98

Step 2: Convert the concentration in moles into concentration in grams. So, in 1 dm³:
Mass in grams = moles × relative formula mass
= 0.04 × 98 = 3.92 g
So the concentration in g/dm³ = 3.92 g/dm³

Example 2: The concentration of a solution of sulfuric acid is 19.6 g/dm³. What is the concentration in MOLES per dm³?

Step 1: The relative formula mass of H_2SO_4 = 98
Step 2: Moles = mass in grams ÷ relative formula mass
= 19.6 ÷ 98 = 0.2 mol   So the concentration in mol/dm³ = 0.2 mol/dm³

Murray wasn't great at concentration.

Numbers? — and you thought you were doing chemistry...

High concentration is like the whole of a rugby team in a mini. Or everyone in Britain living on the Isle of Wight.
Low concentration is like a guy stranded on a desert island, or a small fish in a big lake.

Concentration

Concentration is important. Are you listening... I said concentration is important.

It's Important to Get the Right Concentration

'Diluting' something usually means 'watering it down'.

You might be given a <u>concentrated solution</u> of something and asked to <u>dilute</u> it to make a <u>weaker solution</u>. Don't worry, it's not that complicated:

Example: Explain how you'd produce 500 cm³ of a <u>0.1 mol/dm³</u> solution of KOH (potassium hydroxide) if you're given a <u>1.0 mol/dm³</u> solution of KOH and some water.

Step 1: Work out the RATIO of the two concentrations...
Divide the two concentrations to get a number less than 1.
0.1 ÷ 1.0 = 1/10 ◄— Always divide the small number by the big one.
It's a 1/10 ratio so you'll be doing a 1 in 10 dilution.

Step 2: Multiply this ratio by the volume of solution you want to END UP WITH.
(This tells you how much of your ORIGINAL ACID you need to dilute.)
Volume to dilute = ratio × final volume = 1/10 × 500 = 50 cm³

Step 3: Work out the VOLUME OF WATER you'll need.
Volume of water = total volume – volume to dilute = 500 cm³ – 50 cm³ = 450 cm³

Food Packaging Gives Guideline Daily Amounts (GDAs)

On most food packaging you'll find <u>nutritional information tables</u> — these tell you the amounts of nutrients in the food. <u>Guideline Daily Amounts</u> (GDAs) are the amounts of <u>nutrients</u> that an <u>average adult</u> should eat each day in a healthy diet — food labels often tell you what <u>percentage</u> of various GDAs a product will supply. For example, this information was found on the side of a hot oat cereal packet.

NUTRITIONAL INFORMATION		
	/40 g serving	GDA
Thiamin (B1)	0.5 mg	34%
Riboflavin (B2)	0.5 mg	34%
Calcium	480 mg	60%
Iron	4.8 mg	34%

But the <u>amounts</u> listed may not always be the <u>amount you eat</u>, because...

1) The amounts are given <u>per 100 g</u> (or 100 ml) of the food — but you may eat more or less than this. (The amount <u>per average serving</u> is also sometimes listed — e.g. per 40 g for this cereal.)

2) You may <u>add other things</u> (e.g. milk to cereals — which will increase how much calcium you get).

You Can Use Sodium Content to Estimate the Mass of Salt

You need to be careful how much <u>salt</u> (sodium chloride) you eat. Sometimes salt is included in the nutritional information — but if not, you can <u>estimate</u> it from the mass of <u>sodium</u>...

For example, if a slice of bread contains 0.2 g sodium — how much salt does it contain?
(A_r sodium = 23 and M_r sodium chloride = 58.5)

1) Find the ratio of sodium chloride's M_r to sodium's A_r: 58.5 ÷ 23 = 2.543...

2) Multiply this by the amount of sodium: 2.543... × 0.2 = 0.5086... = <u>0.5 g salt</u>

But the sodium present probably won't all come from sodium chloride — there might be other sodium compounds too, e.g. <u>sodium nitrate</u> (often used as a <u>preservative</u>). So this is probably an <u>overestimate</u>.

This page contains your GDA of concentration calculations...

Why is it that people only read the backs of <u>cereal packets</u>... one of life's little mysteries. Possibly.

Titrations

Titrations are a method of analysing the concentrations of solutions. They're pretty important. Some people don't think they're the most exciting game in town. But I secretly enjoy them, now I've got the hang of them.

Titrations are Used to Find Out Concentrations

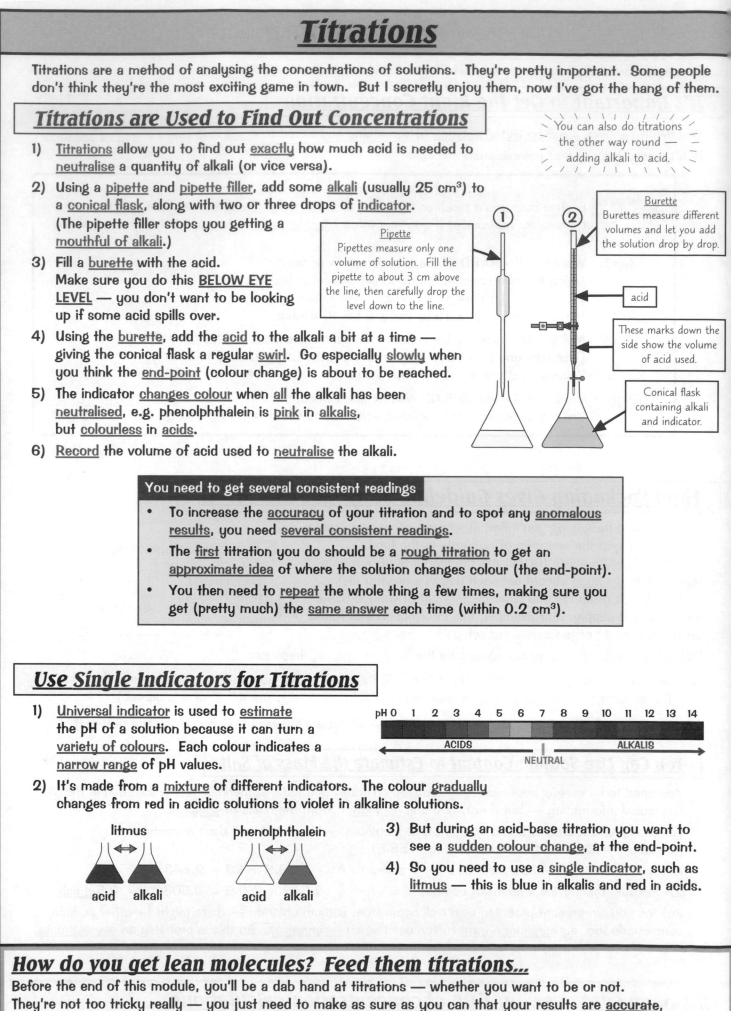

You can also do titrations the other way round — adding alkali to acid.

1) Titrations allow you to find out exactly how much acid is needed to neutralise a quantity of alkali (or vice versa).

2) Using a pipette and pipette filler, add some alkali (usually 25 cm³) to a conical flask, along with two or three drops of indicator. (The pipette filler stops you getting a mouthful of alkali.)

3) Fill a burette with the acid. Make sure you do this BELOW EYE LEVEL — you don't want to be looking up if some acid spills over.

4) Using the burette, add the acid to the alkali a bit at a time — giving the conical flask a regular swirl. Go especially slowly when you think the end-point (colour change) is about to be reached.

5) The indicator changes colour when all the alkali has been neutralised, e.g. phenolphthalein is pink in alkalis, but colourless in acids.

6) Record the volume of acid used to neutralise the alkali.

Pipette
Pipettes measure only one volume of solution. Fill the pipette to about 3 cm above the line, then carefully drop the level down to the line.

Burette
Burettes measure different volumes and let you add the solution drop by drop.

acid

These marks down the side show the volume of acid used.

Conical flask containing alkali and indicator.

You need to get several consistent readings

- To increase the accuracy of your titration and to spot any anomalous results, you need several consistent readings.

- The first titration you do should be a rough titration to get an approximate idea of where the solution changes colour (the end-point).

- You then need to repeat the whole thing a few times, making sure you get (pretty much) the same answer each time (within 0.2 cm³).

Use Single Indicators for Titrations

1) Universal indicator is used to estimate the pH of a solution because it can turn a variety of colours. Each colour indicates a narrow range of pH values.

2) It's made from a mixture of different indicators. The colour gradually changes from red in acidic solutions to violet in alkaline solutions.

pH 0 1 2 3 4 5 6 7 8 9 10 11 12 13 14

ACIDS   NEUTRAL   ALKALIS

litmus

acid   alkali

phenolphthalein

acid   alkali

3) But during an acid-base titration you want to see a sudden colour change, at the end-point.

4) So you need to use a single indicator, such as litmus — this is blue in alkalis and red in acids.

How do you get lean molecules? Feed them titrations...

Before the end of this module, you'll be a dab hand at titrations — whether you want to be or not. They're not too tricky really — you just need to make as sure as you can that your results are accurate, which means going slowly near the end-point and then repeating the whole process.

Titrations

Yes, I know — more on titrations. Complicated stuff this.

pH Curves Show pH Against Volume of Acid or Alkali Added

When you're doing a titration, you'll get a sudden change in pH. So if you plot pH against volume of acid or alkali added, you get a funky S-shape. You need to be able to interpret these pH curves.

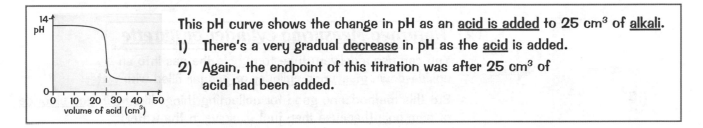

This pH curve shows the change in pH as an alkali is added to 25 cm³ of acid.

1) There's a very gradual increase in pH as the alkali is added.

2) At the endpoint of the titration, there's a sudden change in pH (shown by the nearly vertical line). Here, this happens when 25 cm³ has been added.

3) The volume of alkali needed to neutralise the acid in this example is 25 cm³.

This pH curve shows the change in pH as an acid is added to 25 cm³ of alkali.

1) There's a very gradual decrease in pH as the acid is added.

2) Again, the endpoint of this titration was after 25 cm³ of acid had been added.

You Might be Asked to Calculate the Concentration

In the exam you might be given the results of a titration experiment, and asked to calculate the concentration of the acid when you know the concentration of the alkali (or vice versa).

Example: Say you start off with 25 cm³ of sodium hydroxide (NaOH) in your flask, and you know that its concentration is 0.100 moles per dm³.

You then find from your titration that it takes 49 cm³ of hydrochloric acid (whose concentration you don't know) to neutralise the sodium hydroxide.

You can work out the concentration of the acid in moles per dm³.

Step 1: Work out how many moles of the "known" substance you have:

Number of moles = concentration × volume
= 0.1 mol/dm³ × (25 ÷ 1000) dm³
= 0.0025 moles of sodium hydroxide

Step 2: Write down the balanced equation of the reaction...

NaOH + HCl ⟶ NaCl + H_2O

...and work out how many moles of the "unknown" stuff you must have had.

Using the equation, you can see that for every mole of sodium hydroxide you had...
...there was also one mole of hydrochloric acid.
So if you had 0.0025 moles of sodium hydroxide...
...you must have had 0.0025 moles of hydrochloric acid.

Step 3: Work out the concentration of the "unknown" stuff.
Concentration = number of moles ÷ volume
= 0.0025 mol ÷ (49 ÷ 1000) dm³ = 0.0510 mol/dm³

This is the same formula triangle that's on page 76.

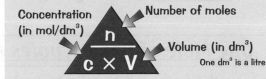

Concentration (in mol/dm³)   Number of moles

$$\frac{n}{c \times V}$$

Volume (in dm³)
One dm³ is a litre

Cover up the thing you're trying to find — then what's left is the formula you need to use.

Don't forget to put the units.

You've got to concentrate whilst doing titrations...

Answer on page 108.

Time for some practice... 25 cm³ of a 0.2 mol/dm³ solution of sulfuric acid, H_2SO_4, was used to neutralise 40 cm³ of calcium hydroxide solution, $Ca(OH)_2$. What's the concentration of calcium hydroxide?

Gas Volumes

The rate of a reaction can be measured by the amount of gas produced. But first it's got to be collected.

The Collection Method Depends on the Gas

In your experiments a <u>conical flask</u> is the standard apparatus to use when you're trying to collect gases produced by a reaction. But what you <u>connect</u> to the flask depends on what it is you're trying to collect...

① Gas Syringe

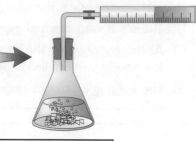

You can use a <u>gas syringe</u> to collect pretty much <u>any</u> gas. Gas syringes usually give volumes accurate to the <u>nearest cm³</u>, so they're pretty accurate. You have to be quite careful though — if the reaction is too <u>vigorous</u>, you can easily blow the plunger out the end of the syringe.

② Upturned Measuring Cylinder or Burette

You can use a delivery tube to <u>bubble</u> the gas into an upside-down <u>measuring cylinder</u> or gas jar filled with <u>water</u>.

But this method's no good for collecting things like <u>hydrogen chloride</u> or <u>ammonia</u> (because they just <u>dissolve</u> in the water).

You can also use an upturned <u>burette</u>, which is a bit more <u>accurate</u> — you can measure to the nearest 0.1 cm³.

You Can Measure the Mass of Gas Produced Too

1) You can measure the <u>mass of gas</u> that a reaction produces by carrying out the experiment on a <u>mass balance</u>.

2) As the gas is released, the mass <u>disappearing</u> is easily measured on the balance.

3) This is the <u>most accurate</u> of the three methods described on this page because the mass balance is very accurate. But it has the <u>disadvantage</u> of releasing the gas straight into the room.

One Mole of Gas Occupies a Volume of 24 dm³

<u>Learn</u> this fact — you're going to <u>need</u> it:

> *Remember dm³ is just a fancy way of writing 'litre', so 1 dm³ = 1000 cm³*

> <u>One mole</u> of <u>any gas</u> always occupies <u>24 dm³</u> (= 24 000 cm³) at room temperature and pressure (RTP = 25 °C and 1 atmosphere)

Example 1: What's the volume of 4.5 moles of chlorine at RTP?

Answer: 1 mole = 24 dm³, so 4.5 moles = 4.5 × 24 dm³ = <u>108 dm³</u>

$$\frac{\text{Volume}}{\text{Moles} \times 24}$$

Example 2: How many moles are there in 8280 cm³ of hydrogen gas at RTP?

Answer: Number of moles = $\dfrac{\text{Volume of gas}}{\text{Volume of 1 mole}}$ = $\dfrac{8.28}{24}$ = <u>0.345 moles</u>

Don't forget to convert from cm³ to dm³.

Pity there's no laughing gas around...

Measuring the mass of gas is more <u>accurate</u> than measuring the volume. Some gas will always escape between starting the reaction and managing to get the bung into the conical flask. There's no way you can do it fast enough. I doubt even Superman could... well, maybe he could.

Following Reactions

If you <u>follow a reaction</u> you can work out loads of stuff — when it stopped, how fast it was, what it had for tea.

Reactions Stop When One Reactant is Used Up

When some <u>magnesium carbonate</u> ($MgCO_3$) is dropped into a beaker of <u>hydrochloric acid</u>, you can tell a <u>reaction</u> is taking place because you see lots of <u>bubbles of gas</u> being given off.

After a while, the amount of fizzing <u>slows down</u> and the reaction eventually <u>stops</u>...

1) The reaction stops when all of one of the reactants is <u>used up</u>. Any other reactants are in <u>excess</u>.

2) The reactant that's <u>used up</u> in a reaction is called the <u>limiting reactant</u>.
   (If the limiting reactant was the acid, you'd see unreacted $MgCO_3$ in the bottom of the flask.)

3) The amount of product formed is <u>directly proportional</u> to the amount of <u>limiting reactant</u>. For example, if you <u>halve</u> the amount of limiting reactant the volume of gas produced will also <u>halve</u>. If you <u>double</u> the amount of limiting reactant the volume of gas will <u>double</u> (as long as it is still the limiting reactant).

4) This is because if you add <u>more reactant</u> there will be <u>more reactant particles</u> to take part in the reaction, which means <u>more product particles</u>.

You've Got to be Able to Read Graphs and Tables...

In this experiment, some <u>magnesium carbonate</u> was added to a solution of <u>hydrochloric acid</u>.
Any gases released were <u>collected</u> using a <u>gas syringe</u> (see p48) — the <u>volume</u> was recorded every 10 s.

Time (s)	0	10	20	30	40	50	60	70	80	90
Volume of gas (cm^3)	0	34	58	76	84	90	94	96	96	96

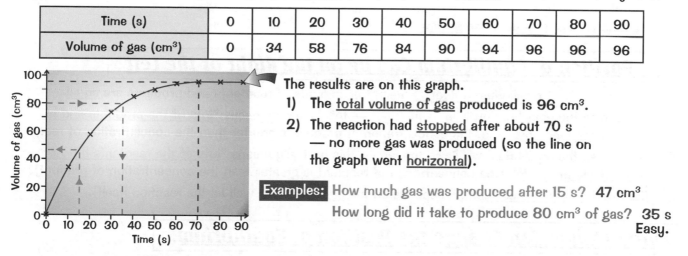

The results are on this graph.

1) The <u>total volume of gas</u> produced is 96 cm^3.

2) The reaction had <u>stopped</u> after about 70 s — no more gas was produced (so the line on the graph went <u>horizontal</u>).

Examples: How much gas was produced after 15 s? 47 cm^3
How long did it take to produce 80 cm^3 of gas? **35 s**
Easy.

Faster Rates of Reaction are Shown by Steeper Curves

If the above reaction had been <u>quicker</u>, the graph would have been <u>steeper</u>.
(The rate of reaction depends on the <u>conditions</u> it's carried out in — see p49-50.)

You might get asked to sketch graphs like these so make sure you understand why they are different.

1) <u>Reaction 1</u> on the right represents a <u>fairly slow</u> reaction. It's not too steep.

2) <u>Reactions 1, 2 and 3</u> all produce the <u>same amount</u> of <u>product</u> (the lines go horizontal at the same height) — this shows they all have the <u>same amount</u> of <u>limiting reactant</u>. But lines 2 and 3 are <u>steeper</u>, which shows that the reactions are happening <u>more quickly</u>.

3) <u>Reaction 4</u> produces <u>more product</u> as well as going <u>faster</u>. This can <u>only</u> happen if there's <u>more</u> of the <u>limiting reactant</u>.

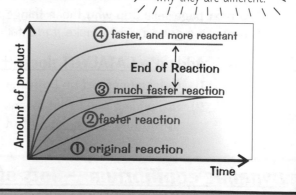

Reactions always slow down — no stamina, you see...

Reactions always go <u>fastest</u> right at the <u>beginning</u> — it's when there are the <u>highest concentrations</u> of reactants.
The reactants eventually run out, or at least one of them does. Nothing ever lasts. Sigh...

Equilibrium

A <u>reversible reaction</u> is one where the <u>products</u> can react with each other and <u>convert back</u> to the original chemicals. In other words, <u>it can go both ways</u>.

> *A <u>REVERSIBLE REACTION</u> is one where the <u>PRODUCTS</u> of the reaction can <u>THEMSELVES REACT</u> to produce the <u>ORIGINAL REACTANTS</u>*
>
> $$A + B \rightleftharpoons C + D$$
>
> The '$\rightleftharpoons$' shows the reaction goes <u>both ways</u>.

Reversible Reactions Will Reach Equilibrium

1) As the <u>reactants</u> (A and B) react, their concentrations <u>fall</u> — so the <u>forward reaction</u> will <u>slow down</u>. But as more and more <u>products</u> (C and D) are made and their concentrations <u>rise</u>, the <u>backward reaction</u> will <u>speed up</u>.

2) After a while the forward reaction will be going at <u>exactly the same rate</u> as the backward one — this is <u>equilibrium</u>.

3) At equilibrium <u>both</u> reactions are still <u>happening</u>, but there's <u>no overall effect</u> (it's a dynamic equilibrium). This means the <u>concentrations</u> of reactants and products have reached a balance and <u>won't change</u>.

4) Equilibrium is only reached if the reversible reaction takes place in a '<u>closed system</u>'. A <u>closed system</u> just means that none of the reactants or products can <u>escape</u>.

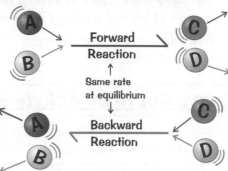

The Position of Equilibrium Can be on the Right or the Left

When a reaction's at equilibrium it <u>doesn't</u> mean the amounts of reactants and products are <u>equal</u>.

1) Sometimes the equilibrium will <u>lie to the right</u> — this basically means "<u>lots of the products and not much of the reactants</u>" (i.e. the concentration of product is greater than the concentration of reactant).

2) Sometimes the equilibrium will <u>lie to the left</u> — this basically means "<u>lots of the reactants but not much of the products</u>" (the concentration of reactant is greater than the concentration of product).

3) The exact <u>position of equilibrium</u> depends on the <u>conditions</u> (as well as the reaction itself).

Three Things Can Change the Position of Equilibrium:

> 1) <u>TEMPERATURE</u>
> 2) <u>PRESSURE</u> (only affects equilibria involving gases)
> 3) <u>CONCENTRATION</u>

1 <u>equilibrium</u>, but 2 <u>equilibria</u>.

The next page tells you <u>why</u> these things affect the equilibrium position — for now just learn that they do. But now's a good time to make a mental note of this potential elephant trap...

> <u>Adding a CATALYST doesn't change the equilibrium position</u>:
>
> 1) Catalysts speed up <u>both</u> the <u>forward</u> and <u>backward</u> reactions by the <u>same amount</u>.
>
> 2) So, adding a catalyst means the reaction reaches equilibrium <u>quicker</u>, but you end up with the <u>same amount</u> of product as you would without the catalyst.

*Dynamic equilibrium — lots of activity, but not to any great effect...**

Many important <u>industrial</u> reactions (e.g. the Haber process — see p42) are reversible. But chances are, just sticking the reactants together into a sealed box won't give a very good <u>yield</u> (i.e. not much product). So what you do is change the <u>conditions</u> — if you do it right, you get more products, and so more money. And that keeps the <u>accountants</u> happy, which, after all, is the main thing in life.

* Much like the England football team.

Changing Equilibrium

Now here's an interesting thing — if you <u>change</u> the conditions, the equilibrium will try to <u>counteract</u> that change. So if you <u>decrease</u> the <u>temperature</u>, the equilibrium will move to <u>produce more heat</u>. Sneaky.

The Equilibrium Tries to Minimise Any Changes You Make

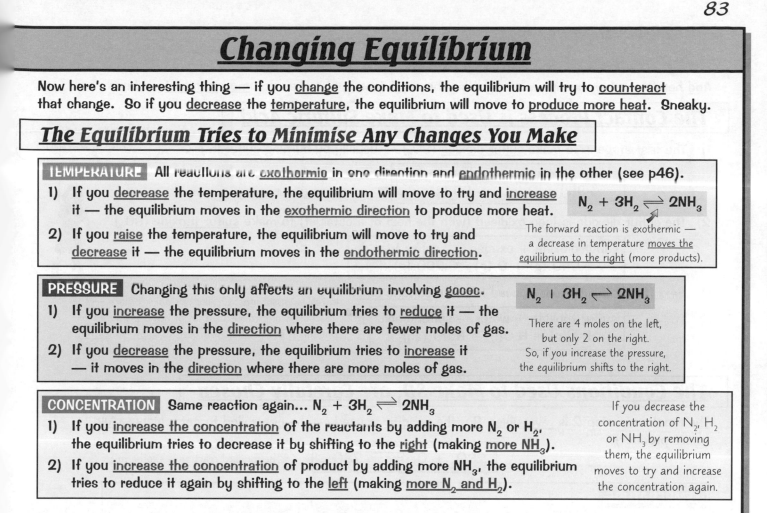

TEMPERATURE All reactions are <u>exothermic</u> in one direction and <u>endothermic</u> in the other (see p46).

1) If you <u>decrease</u> the temperature, the equilibrium will move to try and <u>increase</u> it — the equilibrium moves in the <u>exothermic direction</u> to produce more heat.

$$N_2 + 3H_2 \rightleftharpoons 2NH_3$$

2) If you <u>raise</u> the temperature, the equilibrium will move to try and <u>decrease</u> it — the equilibrium moves in the <u>endothermic direction</u>.

The forward reaction is exothermic — a decrease in temperature <u>moves the equilibrium to the right</u> (more products).

PRESSURE Changing this only affects an equilibrium involving <u>gases</u>.

1) If you <u>increase</u> the pressure, the equilibrium tries to <u>reduce</u> it — the equilibrium moves in the <u>direction</u> where there are fewer moles of gas.

$$N_2 + 3H_2 \rightleftharpoons 2NH_3$$

2) If you <u>decrease</u> the pressure, the equilibrium tries to <u>increase</u> it — it moves in the <u>direction</u> where there are more moles of gas.

There are 4 moles on the left, but only 2 on the right. So, if you increase the pressure, the equilibrium shifts to the right.

CONCENTRATION Same reaction again... $N_2 + 3H_2 \rightleftharpoons 2NH_3$

1) If you <u>increase the concentration</u> of the reactants by adding more N_2 or H_2, the equilibrium tries to decrease it by shifting to the <u>right</u> (making <u>more NH_3</u>).

2) If you <u>increase the concentration</u> of product by adding more NH_3, the equilibrium tries to reduce it again by shifting to the <u>left</u> (making <u>more N_2 and H_2</u>).

If you decrease the concentration of N_2, H_2 or NH_3 by removing them, the equilibrium moves to try and increase the concentration again.

Make Sure You Can Read Equilibrium Tables and Graphs

You might be asked to <u>interpret data</u> about <u>equilibrium</u>, so you'd better know what you're doing. The Haber process (see page 42) is a great example of all this...

$$N_2 + 3H_2 \rightleftharpoons 2NH_3$$ ⟵ The forward reaction is exothermic.

First off, a table...

Pressure (atmospheres)	100	200	300	400	500
% of ammonia in reaction mixture at 450 °C	14	26	34	39	42

1) As the <u>pressure increases</u>, the proportion of ammonia <u>increases</u> (exactly what you'd expect — since increasing the pressure shifts the equilibrium to the side with fewer moles of gas — here, the right).

And now a graph...

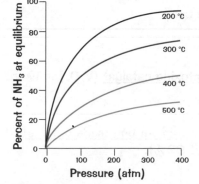

2) This time, each different line represents a different temperature.

3) As the temperature <u>increases</u>, the proportion of ammonia <u>decreases</u> (the backward reaction is endothermic, so this speeds up to try and reduce the temperature again).

4) The conditions that will give you <u>most ammonia</u> are <u>high pressure</u> and <u>low temperature</u>.

An equilibrium is like a particularly stubborn mule...

It's good science this stuff. <u>You</u> do one thing, and the <u>reaction</u> does the other. On the face of it, that sounds like it'd be pretty <u>annoying</u>, but in reality it's what gives you <u>control</u> of what happens. And in <u>industry</u>, control is what makes the whole shebang profitable. Mmmm... Money.

The Contact Process

And here's another example where getting the conditions right makes you <u>more product</u>. Whoop.

The Contact Process is Used to Make Sulfuric Acid

1) The first stage is to make <u>sulfur dioxide</u> (SO_2) — usually by burning <u>sulfur</u> in <u>air</u>.

> sulfur + oxygen → sulfur dioxide
> $S(s) + O_2(g) \rightarrow SO_2(g)$

See page 87 if you don't know what the (s), (l), (g) and (aq) symbols mean.

This isn't the contact process I wanted to learn about...

2) The sulfur dioxide is then <u>oxidised</u> (with the help of a catalyst) to make <u>sulfur trioxide</u> (SO_3).

> sulfur dioxide + oxygen ⇌ sulfur trioxide
> $2SO_2(g) + O_2(g) \rightleftharpoons 2SO_3(g)$

3) Next, the sulfur trioxide is used to make <u>sulfuric acid</u>.

> sulfur trioxide + water → sulfuric acid
> $SO_3(g) + H_2O(l) \rightarrow H_2SO_4(aq)$

In reality, dissolving SO_3 like this doesn't work — the reaction is dangerous as a lot of heat's produced — but this is the reaction you need to <u>know</u>, so <u>learn it</u>. (In practice, you dissolve SO_3 in sulfuric acid first.)

The Conditions Used to Make SO₃ are Carefully Chosen

The reaction in step 2 is <u>reversible</u>. So, the <u>conditions</u> used can be <u>controlled</u> to get a <u>higher yield</u> (more product).

> $2SO_2 + O_2 \rightleftharpoons 2SO_3$

The forward reaction is exothermic.

TEMPERATURE

1) Oxidising sulfur dioxide to form sulfur trioxide is <u>exothermic</u> (it <u>gives out</u> heat).

2) So to get <u>more product</u> you'd think the temperature should be <u>reduced</u> (so the equilibrium will shift to the <u>right</u> to <u>replace the heat</u>).

3) Unfortunately, reducing the temperature <u>slows</u> the reaction right down — not much good.

4) So a <u>compromise</u> temperature of <u>450 °C</u> is used — to get quite a high yield quite quickly.

PRESSURE

1) There are <u>two moles</u> of <u>product</u>, compared to <u>three moles</u> of <u>reactants</u>.

2) So to get <u>more product</u>, you'd think the pressure should be <u>increased</u> (so that the equilibrium will shift to the <u>right</u> to <u>reduce the pressure</u>).

3) But increasing the pressure is <u>expensive</u>, and as the equilibrium is already on the right, it's not really <u>necessary</u>.

4) In fact, <u>atmospheric pressure</u> (1 atmosphere) is used.

CATALYST

1) To <u>increase</u> the rate of reaction a <u>vanadium pentoxide catalyst</u> (V_2O_5) is used.

2) It <u>DOESN'T</u> change the <u>position</u> of the equilibrium.

With a <u>fairly high temperature</u>, a <u>low pressure</u> and a <u>vanadium pentoxide catalyst</u>, the reaction goes <u>pretty quickly</u> and you get a <u>good yield</u> of SO_3 (about 99%).

And that's how chemistry works in real life.

The lonely hearts column — go on, start the contact process...

It's a tough one... do you <u>raise</u> the <u>temperature</u> to get a <u>faster</u> rate of reaction, or <u>reduce</u> it to get a better <u>yield</u>... In the end you <u>compromise</u> (as is so often the case in life... sigh). And that's before you even start to worry about the <u>cost</u> of raising the temperature. Decisions, decisions...

Strong and Weak Acids

Right then. Acids. Brace yourself.

Acids Produce Protons in Water

The thing about acids is that they ionise — they produce hydrogen ions, H^+.
For example,

An H^+ ion is just a proton.

$$HCl \rightarrow H^+ + Cl^-$$
$$HNO_3 \rightarrow H^+ + NO_3^-$$

But HCl doesn't produce hydrogen ions until it meets water — so hydrogen chloride gas isn't an acid.

Acids Can be Strong or Weak

1) Strong acids (e.g. sulfuric, hydrochloric and nitric) ionise completely in water. This means loads of H^+ ions are released.

2) Weak acids (e.g. ethanoic, citric and carbonic) do not fully ionise. Only small numbers of H^+ ions are released.

   For example,

   Strong acid: $HCl \longrightarrow H^+ + Cl^-$
   Weak acid: $CH_3COOH \rightleftharpoons H^+ + CH_3COO^-$

   Use a 'reversible reaction' arrow for a weak acid.

3) The ionisation of a weak acid is a reversible reaction, which sets up an equilibrium mixture. Since only a few H^+ ions are released, the equilibrium lies well to the left.

4) The pH of an acid or alkali is a measure of the concentration of H^+ ions in the solution. Strong acids typically have a pH of about 1 or 2, while the pH of a weak acid might be 4, 5 or 6.

5) The pH of an acid or alkali can be measured with a pH meter or with universal indicator paper (or can be estimated by seeing how fast a sample reacts with, say, magnesium).

Don't Confuse Strong Acids with Concentrated Acids

1) Acid strength (i.e. strong or weak) tells you what proportion of the acid molecules ionise in water.

2) The concentration of an acid is different. Concentration measures how many moles of acid there are in a litre ($1 \ dm^3$) of water. Concentration is basically how watered down your acid is.

3) Note that concentration describes the total number of dissolved acid molecules — not the number of molecules that produce hydrogen ions.

4) The more moles of acid per dm^3, the more concentrated the acid is.

5) So you can have a dilute but strong acid, or a concentrated but weak acid.

Strong Acids are Better Electrical Conductors than Weak Acids

1) Ethanoic acid has a much lower electrical conductivity than the same concentration of hydrochloric acid. It's all to do with the concentration of the ions.

2) It's the ions that carry the charge through the acid solutions as they move. So the lower concentration of ions in the weak acid means less charge can be carried. Simple.

3) Electrolysis of hydrochloric acid or ethanoic acid produces H_2 because they both produce H^+ ions.

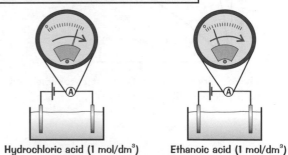

Hydrochloric acid ($1 \ mol/dm^3$)   Ethanoic acid ($1 \ mol/dm^3$)

Concentration — oh so important when revising chemistry...

Acids are acidic because of H^+ ions. And strong acids are strong because they let go of all their H^+ ions at the drop of a hat... well, at the drop of a drop of water. This is tricky — no doubt about it, but if you can get your head round this, then you can probably cope with just about anything.

Strong and Weak Acids

Here's a nice bit of science... not the easiest thing in the book, but I like it.

Strong Acids React Faster Than Weak Acids

Strong and weak acids react with reactive metals and with carbonates in the same way.

1) Both <u>hydrochloric acid</u> (strong) and <u>ethanoic acid</u> (weak) will react with <u>magnesium</u> to give <u>hydrogen</u>.

$$2HCl + Mg \rightarrow MgCl_2 + H_2$$
$$2CH_3COOH + Mg \rightarrow Mg(CH_3COO)_2 + H_2$$

And both <u>hydrochloric acid</u> and <u>ethanoic acid</u> will react with <u>calcium carbonate</u> to give <u>carbon dioxide</u>.

$$2HCl + CaCO_3 \rightarrow CaCl_2 + H_2O + CO_2$$
$$2CH_3COOH + CaCO_3 \rightarrow Ca(CH_3COO)_2 + H_2O + CO_2$$

2) The <u>difference</u> between the reactions of the two acids will be the <u>rate of reaction</u>. Ethanoic acid will react <u>more slowly</u> than hydrochloric acid of the <u>same concentration</u>.

3) It's all to do with the <u>equilibrium</u> in the <u>weak acid</u> reaction ($CH_3COOH \rightleftharpoons H^+ + CH_3COO^-$).

4) When you put a <u>weak acid</u> into water, it releases <u>a few</u> H^+ ions, but the concentration of H^+ ions is low compared to what you'd get with a strong acid. So when you add magnesium (or calcium carbonate), the <u>collision frequency</u> between the reactants is <u>low</u>.

5) When the H^+ ions react the <u>concentration</u> of H^+ ions <u>decreases</u>, so the equilibrium shifts to <u>compensate</u> — meaning a few <u>more</u> H^+ ions are released. These ions then react, so the equilibrium shifts... and so on. As more ions are <u>removed</u>, more are <u>supplied</u> — kind of a <u>drip-feed</u> arrangement.

6) This is <u>completely</u> different to what you get with a <u>strong</u> acid, where <u>all</u> of the acid molecules are ionised and loads of H^+ ions are just sitting there ready and waiting to go. So when you add magnesium (or calcium carbonate), the <u>collision frequency</u> between the reactants is really <u>high</u>.

The Volume of Gas Produced Depends Upon the Amount of Acid

1) Hydrochloric acid (strong) will react <u>faster</u> than ethanoic acid (weak), but the <u>amount of product</u> you get will be the <u>same</u> (if you start with the same amount and they're the same concentration, etc.).

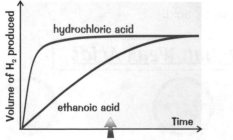

Hydrochloric acid reacts faster (steeper curve), but both reactions give the same amount of hydrogen.

2) This is because if the <u>concentrations</u> are the <u>same</u>, the number of <u>molecules</u> in a litre (say) of water will be the same.

3) And each of these molecules can let go of <u>one</u> H^+ ion.

$$HCl \longrightarrow H^+ + Cl^-, \text{ and } CH_3COOH \rightleftharpoons H^+ + CH_3COO^-$$

It's just that hydrochloric acid has let go of them <u>all at once</u>, whereas ethanoic acid lets them go <u>gradually</u>.

4) But since the <u>total</u> number of H^+ ions available is the <u>same</u>, the <u>volume of gaseous product</u> will be the same (it's the H^+ ions that are the important bits in acid reactions).

Jumping jack flash, HCl makes gas...

Hydrochloric acid is nasty stuff. It's <u>corrosive</u> and <u>irritating</u>, damages almost everything it touches and will <u>burn</u> skin. Yet we have it in our stomachs. Luckily we have a thick layer of <u>mucus</u> to protect our stomach walls.

Precipitation Reactions

Precipitates don't dissolve, remember...

Precipitation Reactions Make an Insoluble Substance

1) Precipitation reactions normally involve <u>two solutions reacting</u> together to make an <u>insoluble substance</u>.

2) The insoluble substance is called the <u>precipitate</u>, and it makes the solution turn <u>cloudy</u>.

3) Most precipitation reactions involve <u>ions</u>. To react with each other, these ions need to collide, so they have to be able to move.

4) This means the ionic substances have to be <u>in solution</u> or <u>molten</u> as the ions in <u>solid</u> ionic substances <u>can't move</u>.

5) These reactions are usually <u>extremely quick</u> because there is a <u>high collision frequency</u> between the ions.

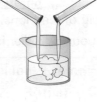

Ionic Equations Show Just the Useful Bits of Reactions

Look at this precipitation reaction...

barium chloride + sodium sulfate → barium sulfate + sodium chloride
$BaCl_2$ (aq) + Na_2SO_4 (aq) → $BaSO_4$ (s) + 2NaCl (aq)

The (aq) and the (s) are <u>state symbols</u> — make sure you know them.
(s) = solid,
(l) = liquid,
(g) = gas,
(aq) = aqueous (dissolved in water)

1) You can tell it's a <u>precipitation</u> reaction because you start off with <u>two solutions</u> (look at the <u>state symbols</u> — they're both 'aq'), but you end up with a <u>solid</u>. This solid is the precipitate — it'll turn the water <u>cloudy</u>.

2) The 'interesting' bit of this reaction is the bit involving the <u>barium</u> and the <u>sulfate</u> ions — it's these that form the precipitate.

3) The <u>sodium</u> and <u>chloride</u> ions were dissolved in solution <u>before</u> the reaction, and they're still dissolved <u>afterwards</u>. They're called <u>spectator ions</u> because they <u>don't change</u> during the reaction.

4) An <u>ionic equation</u> concentrates on the interesting bits of a reaction, and ignores the spectator ions. So the ionic equation for this equation would be:

$$Ba^{2+}(aq) + SO_4^{2-} (aq) → BaSO_4 (s)$$

Test for Sulfates (SO_4^{2-}) and Halides (Cl^-, Br^-, I^-)

You can use precipitation reactions to try and <u>identify</u> mystery substances.
The <u>colour</u> of any precipitate can help you decide what <u>ions</u> are present.

Test for Sulfate ions, (SO_4^{2-})

1) To test for a <u>sulfate</u> ion, SO_4^{2-}, <u>add dilute HCl</u>, followed by <u>barium chloride</u>, $BaCl_2$.

2) A <u>white</u> precipitate of <u>barium sulfate</u> means the original compound was a sulfate.
$$Ba^{2+}(aq) + SO_4^{2-}(aq) \longrightarrow BaSO_4(s)$$

3) For example, adding HCl and barium chloride to <u>potassium sulfate</u>, K_2SO_4, or <u>magnesium sulfate</u>, $MgSO_4$, will produce a <u>white</u> precipitate.

Test for Chloride (Cl^-), Bromide (Br^-) or Iodide (I^-) ions

To test for <u>chloride</u>, <u>bromide</u> or <u>iodide</u> ions, add <u>dilute nitric acid</u>, HNO_3, followed by <u>lead nitrate</u>, $Pb(NO_3)_2$.

A <u>chloride</u> gives a white precipitate of <u>lead chloride</u>. $Pb^{2+}(aq) + 2Cl^-(aq) \longrightarrow PbCl_2(s)$

A <u>bromide</u> gives a cream precipitate of <u>lead bromide</u>. $Pb^{2+}(aq) + 2Br^-(aq) \longrightarrow PbBr_2(s)$

An <u>iodide</u> gives a yellow precipitate of <u>lead iodide</u>. $Pb^{2+}(aq) + 2I^-(aq) \longrightarrow PbI_2(s)$

If you aren't part of the solution, you're part of the precipitate...

Think of an ionic equation as a bit like Match of the Day — just an <u>edited highlights package</u>.

Preparing Insoluble Salts

You can use <u>precipitation reactions</u> to make <u>insoluble salts</u>.
You just need to pick the right reactants, then mix them together.

Pick the Right Reactants...

1) To make an insoluble salt you need some <u>ions</u> — e.g. to make <u>lead iodide</u> (PbI_2), you need some <u>lead ions</u> and some <u>iodide ions</u>. And these ions need to be in <u>solution</u>, so they can <u>move</u> about.

2) Fortunately, <u>nitrates</u> are <u>soluble</u> — so if you use a solution of <u>lead nitrate</u> ($Pb(NO_3)_2$), you have your supply of lead ions. You can get your iodide ions from, say, <u>potassium iodide</u> (KI).

3) Mix your ingredients together, and voilà — you have yourself an insoluble salt. Here's the reaction.

lead nitrate + potassium iodide	$\rightarrow$	lead iodide	+	potassium nitrate
$Pb(NO_3)_2$ (aq) + 2KI (aq)	$\rightarrow$	PbI_2 (s)	+	$2KNO_3$ (aq)

Or even...

$$Pb^{2+} \text{ (aq) } + 2I^- \text{ (aq)} \rightarrow PbI_2 \text{ (s)}$$

4) If this is <u>all</u> you do, your salt will be <u>wet</u>, and <u>mixed in</u> with other stuff. The method below will help you avoid that...

...Then Precipitate, Filter and Dry

Stage 1

1) Add 1 spatula of <u>lead nitrate</u> to a test tube, and fill it with <u>distilled water</u>. <u>Shake it thoroughly</u> to ensure that all the lead nitrate has <u>dissolved</u>. Then do the same with 1 spatula of <u>potassium iodide</u>. (Use distilled water to make sure there are <u>no other ions</u> about.)

2) Tip the <u>two solutions</u> into a small beaker, and give it a good stir to make sure it's all mixed together. The salt should <u>precipitate</u> out.

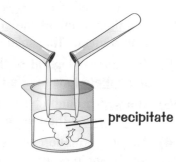

precipitate

Stage 2

filter paper

filter funnel

1) Put a folded piece of <u>filter paper</u> into a <u>filter funnel</u>, and stick the funnel into a <u>conical flask</u>.

2) <u>Pour</u> the contents of the beaker into the middle of the filter paper. (Make sure that the solution doesn't go above the filter paper — otherwise some of the solid could dribble down the side.)

3) <u>Swill out</u> the beaker with more distilled water, and tip this into the filter paper — to make sure you get <u>all the product</u> from the beaker.

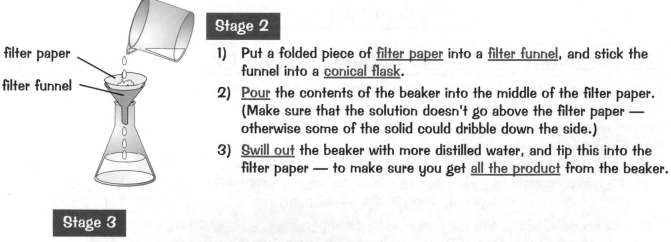

Stage 3

1) Rinse the contents of the filter paper with distilled water to make sure that <u>all the soluble salts</u> have been washed away.

2) Then just scrape the <u>lead iodide</u> on to some fresh filter paper and leave it to dry.

lead iodide

Get two solutions, mix 'em together — job's a good 'un...

Well, wouldn't you know — precipitation reactions can be used for <u>all sorts</u> of things. <u>Testing for ions</u> in solutions, making <u>insoluble salts</u>, and urmm... demonstrating the absolute wonderness of <u>ionic equations</u>. Ah-hem. Never mind. You've gotta learn about them anyway...

Revision Summary for Module C5

Ah, revision summaries... my favourite part of the section. And yours no doubt, since they're always at the end. There are lots of calculations in this section, but that's good (honest), because you can expect a fair few in the exam as well. And as a wise man once said... it's best to practise before the exam, because once you're in there, it's a bit late really. So get your calculator fired up, and away you go...

1)   What is the formula relating moles, mass and M_r?

2)*   How many moles are there in 284 g of sodium sulfate, Na_2SO_4?

3)*   What mass of chlorine is there in 2 moles of magnesium chloride, $MgCl_2$?

4)   Give the definition of the relative atomic mass of an element.

5)*   Here's the equation for sodium burning in air to produce sodium oxide: $4Na + O_2 \rightarrow 2Na_2O$.
        Use moles to calculate the mass of sodium that is needed to produce 108.2 g of sodium oxide.

6)*   What is an empirical formula? Find the empirical formula of the compound formed when
        21.9 g of magnesium, 29.3 g of sulfur and 58.3 g of oxygen react.

7)*   Calculate the concentration of the solution in g/dm^3 formed when 7.5 g of calcium hydroxide, $Ca(OH)_2$,
        is dissolved in: a) 1 dm^3 of water,   b) 2 dm^3 of water.

8)*   How many moles of barium chloride are in 500 cm^3 of a 0.2 molar solution of barium chloride?

9)*   How would you produce 250 cm^3 of a 0.2 mol/dm^3 solution of sulfuric acid if you were given a
        1.0 mol/dm^3 solution of sulfuric acid, and water?

10)   This nutritional information table was found on an orange juice carton:
        Angela says that one glass will give her 42% of the guideline
        daily amount of vitamin C. Why might she be wrong?

NUTRITIONAL INFORMATION	
Typical values for 100 ml	
Energy	197 kJ
	46 kcal
Carbohydrate	10.4 g
Vitamin C	25 mg (42% GDA)

11)   Why do you need to get several consistent readings in titrations?

12)   Why is a single indicator like phenolphthalein used in titrations?

13)   Sketch a pH curve for the titration where hydrochloric acid is added to sodium hydroxide.

14)* In a titration, 22.5 cm^3 of nitric acid was required to neutralise 25 cm^3
        of potassium hydroxide with a concentration of 0.15 moles per dm^3.
        Calculate the concentration of the nitric acid in: a) mol/dm^3,   b) g/dm^3.

15)   Name 3 methods used for measuring the amount of gas produced in a reaction. Give their advantages.

16)   What volume does one mole of gas take up at room temperature and pressure?

17)   What is the limiting reactant in a reaction?

18)* The graph shows the volume of hydrogen produced when magnesium
        metal was placed into a hydrochloric acid solution.
        a) How much hydrogen had evolved at the end of the reaction?
        b) How long did it take to produce 35 cm^3 of hydrogen?

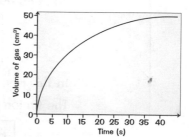

19)   What is a reversible reaction? Explain why it could reach an equilibrium.

20)   Describe how three different factors affect the position of equilibrium.

21)   Write the symbol equations for the three reactions in the Contact Process.

22)   State and explain the conditions used in the Contact Process.

23)   What is the difference between the strength of an acid and its concentration?

24)   Explain why weak acids react slower than strong acids.

25)   What is the ionic equation for the reaction between lead nitrate and sodium bromide?

26)   How would you test for: a) a sulfate, b) a halide?

27)   Describe how you would obtain a dry sample of lead chloride from lead nitrate and calcium chloride.

* Answers on page 108.

Redox Reactions

In chemistry, things get oxidised and reduced all the time. And you need to learn about it.

If Electrons are Transferred, It's a Redox Reaction

1) Oxidation can mean the <u>addition of oxygen</u> (or a reaction with it), and reduction can be the <u>removal of oxygen</u>, but on this page we're looking at oxidation and reduction in terms of <u>electrons</u>.

2) A <u>loss of electrons</u> is called <u>oxidation</u>. A <u>gain of electrons</u> is called <u>reduction</u>.

3) REDuction and OXidation happen <u>at the same time</u> — hence the term "REDOX".

4) An <u>oxidising agent</u> accepts electrons and <u>gets reduced</u>.

5) A <u>reducing agent</u> donates electrons and <u>gets oxidised</u>.

> *Remember it as OIL RIG.*
>
> <u>O</u>xidation <u>I</u>s <u>L</u>oss
>
> <u>R</u>eduction <u>I</u>s <u>G</u>ain
>
> (of <u>electrons</u>)

Some Examples of Redox Reactions:

1) <u>Chlorine gas</u> is passed into a solution of an iron(II) salt. The solution turns from green to yellow as the iron(II) ion is oxidised to iron(III). The Fe^{2+} ion <u>loses an electron</u> to form Fe^{3+}.

$$Fe^{2+} - e^- \rightarrow Fe^{3+}$$

2) The <u>chlorine</u> causes this to happen — it's the <u>oxidising agent</u>.

3) The chlorine must've <u>gained</u> the electron that the Fe^{2+} lost. The chlorine's been <u>reduced</u>. The iron(II) ion must be the <u>reducing agent</u>.

$$\tfrac{1}{2}Cl_2 + e^- \rightarrow Cl^-$$

---

1) <u>Iron atoms</u> are <u>oxidised</u> to iron(II) ions when they react with <u>dilute acid</u>.

$$Fe - 2e^- \rightarrow Fe^{2+}$$

2) The <u>iron atoms lose electrons</u>. They're <u>oxidised</u> by the hydrogen ions.

3) The <u>hydrogen ions gain electrons</u>. They're <u>reduced</u> by the iron atoms.

$$2H^+ + 2e^- \rightarrow H_2$$

Displacement Reactions are Redox Reactions

1) <u>Displacement</u> reactions involve one metal <u>kicking another one out</u> of a compound. Learn this rule:

> **A MORE REACTIVE metal will displace a LESS REACTIVE metal from its compound.**

2) If you put a <u>reactive metal</u> into the solution of a <u>dissolved metal compound</u>, the reactive metal will <u>replace</u> the <u>less reactive metal</u> in the compound.

> **Example:** Put <u>iron</u> in a solution of <u>tin(II) sulfate</u> and the more reactive iron will "<u>kick out</u>" the less reactive tin from the solution. You end up with <u>iron(II) sulfate solution</u> and <u>tin metal</u>.
>
> $$\text{iron + tin(II) sulfate} \rightarrow \text{iron(II) sulfate + tin}$$
> $$Fe(s) + SnSO_4(aq) \rightarrow FeSO_4(aq) + Sn(s)$$
>
>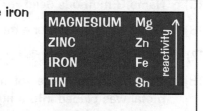
>
> | MAGNESIUM | Mg |
> | ZINC | Zn |
> | IRON | Fe |
> | TIN | Sn |
>
> reactivity ↑
>
> In this reaction the iron <u>loses</u> 2 electrons to become a 2+ ion — it's <u>oxidised</u>.
>
> The tin ion <u>gains</u> these 2 electrons to become a tin atom — it's <u>reduced</u>.
>
> $$Fe + SO_4^{2-} \rightarrow FeSO_4 + 2e^-$$ $$Sn^{2+} + 2e^- \rightarrow Sn$$

3) In displacement reactions it's always the <u>metal ion</u> that gains electrons and is <u>reduced</u>. The <u>metal atom</u> always loses electrons and is <u>oxidised</u>.

4) In the exam you could be asked to write <u>word or symbol equations</u> to show displacement reactions. You could also be asked to <u>predict</u> whether or not a displacement reaction will happen. All you have to remember is that <u>more reactive metals displace less reactive ones</u> and you'll be fine and dandy.

REDOX — great for bubble baths. Oh no, wait...

Try writing some displacement reaction equations now — write the equation for the reaction between <u>zinc and iron chloride</u> ($FeCl_2$). What's being <u>oxidised</u>? What's being <u>reduced</u>? You need to practise till you can <u>do it in your sleep</u>.

Rusting of Iron

Rusting is a <u>favourite topic</u> of examiners everywhere...

Rusting of Iron is a Redox Reaction

1) Iron and some steels will <u>rust</u> if they come into contact with air and water.
   Rusting only happens when the iron's in contact with <u>both oxygen</u> (from the air) and <u>water</u>.

2) Rust is a form of <u>hydrated iron(III) oxide</u>.

3) Learn the <u>equation for rust</u>: ➡️ | iron + oxygen + water → hydrated iron(III) oxide |

4) Rusting of iron is a <u>redox reaction</u>.

5) This is why. <u>Iron loses electrons</u> when it reacts with oxygen.
   Each Fe atom <u>loses three electrons</u> to become Fe^{3+}. Iron's <u>oxidised</u>.

6) <u>Oxygen gains electrons</u> when it reacts with iron.
   Each O atom <u>gains two electrons</u> to become O^{2-}. Oxygen's <u>reduced</u>.

Remember <u>OIL RIG</u>.

Metals are Combined with Other Things to Prevent Rust

1) Iron can be prevented from rusting by mixing it with <u>other metals</u> to make alloys.

2) <u>Steels</u> are alloys of iron with <u>carbon</u> and small quantities of other metals.

3) One of the most common steels is <u>stainless steel</u> — a rustproof alloy of iron, carbon and <u>chromium</u>.

Oil, Grease and Paint Prevent Rusting

You can <u>prevent rusting</u> by coating the iron with a <u>barrier</u>. This <u>keeps out the water</u>, <u>oxygen</u> or <u>both</u>.

1) <u>Painting</u> is ideal for large and small structures. It can also be nice and <u>colourful</u>.

2) <u>Oiling</u> or <u>greasing</u> has to be used when <u>moving parts</u> are involved, like on <u>bike chains</u>.

A Coat of Tin Can Protect Steel from Rust

1) <u>Tin plating</u> is where a coat of tin is applied to the object, e.g. food cans.

2) The tin acts as a <u>barrier</u>, stopping water and oxygen in the air from reaching the <u>surface</u> of the iron.

3) This only works as long as the <u>tin remains intact</u>. If the tin is <u>scratched</u> to reveal some iron, the <u>iron will lose electrons</u> in <u>preference</u> to the tin and the iron will rust even faster than if it was on its own.

4) That's why it's <u>not</u> always a good idea to buy the <u>reduced bashed tins</u> of food at the supermarket. They could be starting to <u>rust</u>.

More Reactive Metals Can Also be Used to Prevent Iron Rusting

You can also prevent rusting using the <u>sacrificial</u> method. You place a <u>more reactive metal</u> with the iron. The water and oxygen then react with this "sacrificial" metal instead of with the iron.

1) <u>Galvanising</u> is where a coat of <u>zinc</u> is put onto the object. The zinc acts as sacrificial protection — it's <u>more reactive</u> than iron so it'll <u>lose electrons in preference</u> to iron. The zinc also acts as a barrier. Steel <u>buckets</u> and <u>corrugated iron roofing</u> are often galvanised.

2) Blocks of metal, e.g. <u>magnesium</u>, can be bolted to the iron. Magnesium will <u>lose electrons in preference to iron</u>. It's used on the hulls of <u>ships</u>, or on <u>underground iron pipes</u>.

Galvanising protects the metal underneath even when the zinc gets scratched.

<u>Don't get confused</u> about sacrificial protection — it's <u>not a displacement reaction</u>. There isn't a metal reacting with a metal salt — oxygen's reacting with a more reactive metal instead of a less reactive one.

Alloy there Jim Lad...

<u>Rust</u> is one of those really annoying things. It eats your bike, your car, your ship... but then doesn't touch that lovely woolly cardigan that your gran gave you. On the plus side though, you can use it to dye your clothes, just place a rusty object on the fabric, add a splash of vinegar, and voilà — a beautiful orange stain. Marvellous.

Electrolysis

It's time for some more _electrolysis_ — but this time it's a little different. Honest. You've got to be able to predict the products of electrolysis using _aqueous_ electrolytes. What are you waiting for...

Electrolysis Means "Splitting Up with Electricity"

1) _Electrolysis_ is the _breaking down_ of a substance using _electricity_ (see page 35).

2) An electric current is passed through a _molten_ or _dissolved_ ionic compound, causing it to _decompose_.

3) This creates a _flow of charge_ through the _electrolyte_.

4) The _positive ions_ in the solution will move towards the _cathode_ (-ve electrode) and _gain_ electrons.

5) The _negative ions_ in the solution will move towards the _anode_ (+ve electrode) and _lose_ electrons.

6) As ions gain or lose electrons they become atoms or molecules and are _discharged_ from the solution at the _electrodes_.

It May be Easier to Discharge Ions from Water than the Solute

1) In _aqueous_ solutions, as well as the ions from the solute (the ionic compound), there are hydrogen ions (H^+) and hydroxide ions (OH^-) from the _water_.

2) Sometimes, it's _easier_ to _discharge_ the ions from the _water_ instead of the ones from the _solute_.

3) This means _hydrogen_ could be produced at the cathode, and _oxygen_ at the anode.

A solution of _aqueous sulfuric acid_ (H_2SO_4) contains _three different ions_: SO_4^{2-}, H^+ and OH^-.

- _Hydrogen ions_ (from the water or sulfuric acid) can accept the electrons (from the cathode). So at the cathode, _hydrogen gas_ is produced.

$$2H^+ + 2e^- \rightarrow H_2$$

- _Hydroxide ions_ (from water) can lose electrons more easily than sulfate ions. So at the anode _oxygen_ is produced.

$$4OH^- - 4e^- \rightarrow O_2 + 2H_2O$$

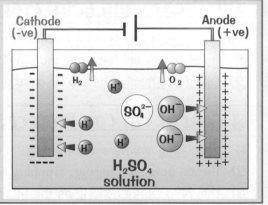

A solution of _aqueous sodium hydroxide_ (NaOH) contains _three different ions_: Na^+, OH^- and H^+.

- _Hydrogen ions_ (from the water) can accept the electrons (from the cathode) more easily than the sodium ions. So at the cathode, _hydrogen gas_ is produced.

$$2H^+ + 2e^- \rightarrow H_2$$

- _Hydroxide ions_ (from water or sodium hydroxide) can lose electrons (to the anode). So at the anode _oxygen_ is produced.

$$4OH^- - 4e^- \rightarrow O_2 + 2H_2O$$

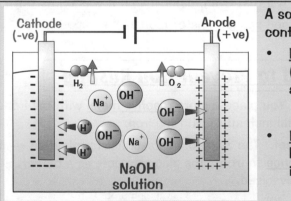

4) The electrolysis of H_2SO_4 and NaOH are both _redox reactions_ — reduction takes place at the cathode and oxidation takes place at the anode.

Everyone needs good electrons...

The hardest bit's over now. Remember that with _aqueous solutions_, there are ions from the dissolved substance _and_ from the water. With H_2SO_4 and NaOH, you get _hydrogen_ and _oxygen_ because it's easier to use the ions from the water than the ones from the solute — just remember that and you'll be fine.

Electrolysis

Just one more example of an aqueous electrolyte then we'll move swiftly on to molten electrolytes. Oh goody.

Copper(II) Sulfate Can be Electrolysed to Form Copper and Oxygen

Here's what happens during the electrolysis of copper(II) sulfate solution when you use carbon electrodes.

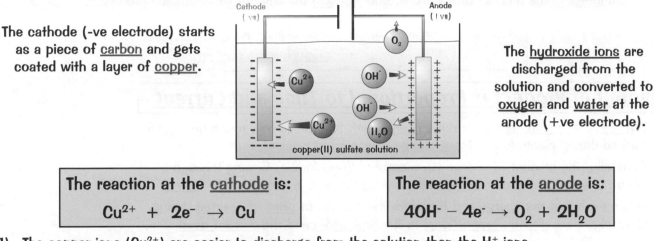

The cathode (-ve electrode) starts as a piece of carbon and gets coated with a layer of copper.

The hydroxide ions are discharged from the solution and converted to oxygen and water at the anode (+ve electrode).

The reaction at the cathode is:	The reaction at the anode is:
$Cu^{2+} + 2e^- \rightarrow Cu$	$4OH^- - 4e^- \rightarrow O_2 + 2H_2O$

1) The copper ions (Cu^{2+}) are easier to discharge from the solution than the H^+ ions.

2) So they are attracted to the negative anode and are reduced to copper atoms (instead of H^+ ions being reduced to H_2).

3) The hydroxide ions are oxidised to oxygen and water at the anode.

4) Pure copper atoms bond to the cathode and form a thin layer of copper over the surface of the carbon electrode.

In Molten Ionic Solids, There's Only One Source of Ions

1) An ionic solid can't be electrolysed because the ions are in fixed positions and can't move.

2) Molten ionic compounds can be electrolysed because the ions can move freely and conduct electricity.

3) Molten ionic liquids are always broken up into their elements.

4) Positive metal ions are reduced (i.e. they gain electrons) to atoms at the cathode:

$$Pb^{2+} + 2e^- \rightarrow Pb$$

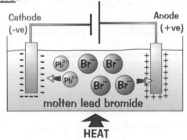

You can melt lead bromide using a Bunsen burner.

5) Negative ions are oxidised (i.e. they lose electrons) to atoms at the anode:

$$2Br^- \rightarrow Br_2 + 2e^-$$

6) It's easy to predict what products you get when you electrolyse molten substances — it's getting the half-equations right that's difficult. Learn these to get a head start:

Molten Electrolyte	Product Produced at Cathode	Half-Equation at Cathode	Product Produced at Anode	Half-Equation at Anode
lead iodide, PbI_2	lead	$Pb^{2+} + 2e^- \rightarrow Pb$	iodine	$2I^- \rightarrow I_2 + 2e^-$
potassium chloride, KCl	potassium	$K^+ + e^- \rightarrow K$	chlorine	$2Cl^- \rightarrow Cl_2 + 2e^-$
aluminium oxide, Al_2O_3	aluminium	$Al^{3+} + 3e^- \rightarrow Al$	oxygen	$2O^{2-} \rightarrow O_2 + 4e^-$

Which element does a robber fear most? Copper...

There's an awful lot on this page and the best way to learn it is to cover, scribble, check. You know it works.

Electrolysis

Here come the calculations. Run... while you still can...

Number of Electrons Transferred Increases with Time and Current

1) The amount of product made during electrolysis depends on the number of electrons that are transferred.

2) If you increase the number of electrons, you increase the amount of substance produced.

> This can be achieved by:
> • electrolysing for a longer time.
> • increasing the current.

Amount of Product is Proportional to Time and Current

1) Current is a flow of charge, and it's charge that determines how much product is formed during electrolysis. More charge means more product.

2) Generally, the amount of charge (Q, measured in coulombs) flowing through a circuit is equal to the current (I) multiplied by the time in seconds (t): $Q = It$

3) This means that the charge and therefore the amount of product created during electrolysis are directly proportional to the time taken and the current used.

You Can Use Q = It to Work Out the Amount of Product Formed

Example 1: In an electrolysis experiment, a current of 2.0 A is passed through the electrolyte for 40 seconds. Calculate the amount of charge flowing through the circuit.

Method: This one's simple, you just have to use the equation $Q = It$.

$Q = I \times t = 2.0\,A \times 40\ seconds = \underline{80.0\ coulombs}$. Simple. Now lets try a more tricky one...

Example 2: Dorothy is conducting an electrolysis experiment using aqueous tin(II) chloride ($SnCl_2$). She collects the chlorine from the reaction in a test tube held above the anode and measures the time taken to fill the test tube. She runs three different experiments changing the current used each time. Her results are shown below.

Experiment	Current in amps	Time taken to fill test tube in seconds
A	0.5	100
B	1	50
C	2	?

Use the information in the table to work out the time taken for the test tube to fill up with chlorine in experiment C.

Method: First, work out the charge using $Q = It$ and the data from experiment A.

$Q = It = 0.5 \times 100 = 50\ coulombs$.

Then use this value to work out the time taken in experiment C. You just have to rearrange the equation so you can find t.

$t = Q \div I = 50 \div 2 = \underline{25\ seconds}$.

> You'll get the same answer if you use the data from experiment B.

If you can remember that the time is inversely proportional to the current you can skip a few steps of the calculation. From experiment A to experiment C the current has increased by a factor of underline{4}. If they're inversely proportional this means that the time will have to decrease by a factor of underline{4}. $100 \div 4 = \underline{25\ seconds}$. Job done.

The more time you spend on this page, the more you'll learn...

This stuff isn't easy — in fact it's devilishly complicated. So take your time over it. Read it through once. If you don't get it, read it through again. If you still don't get it, have a cup of tea before reading it again. That should help.

Fuel Cells

Fuel cells are great — they use hydrogen and oxygen to make electricity.

Hydrogen and Oxygen Give Out Energy When They React

1) Hydrogen and oxygen react to produce water.

2) The reaction between hydrogen and oxygen is exothermic — it releases energy.

3) You can show this on an energy level diagram.

4) The higher a line is on the diagram the more energy the substances have. For example the H_2 and O_2 molecules have a higher energy than the H_2O molecules.

5) When the new bonds are formed the excess energy is given out in the form of heat.

6) You could be asked to interpret energy level diagrams for other reactions too. For example:

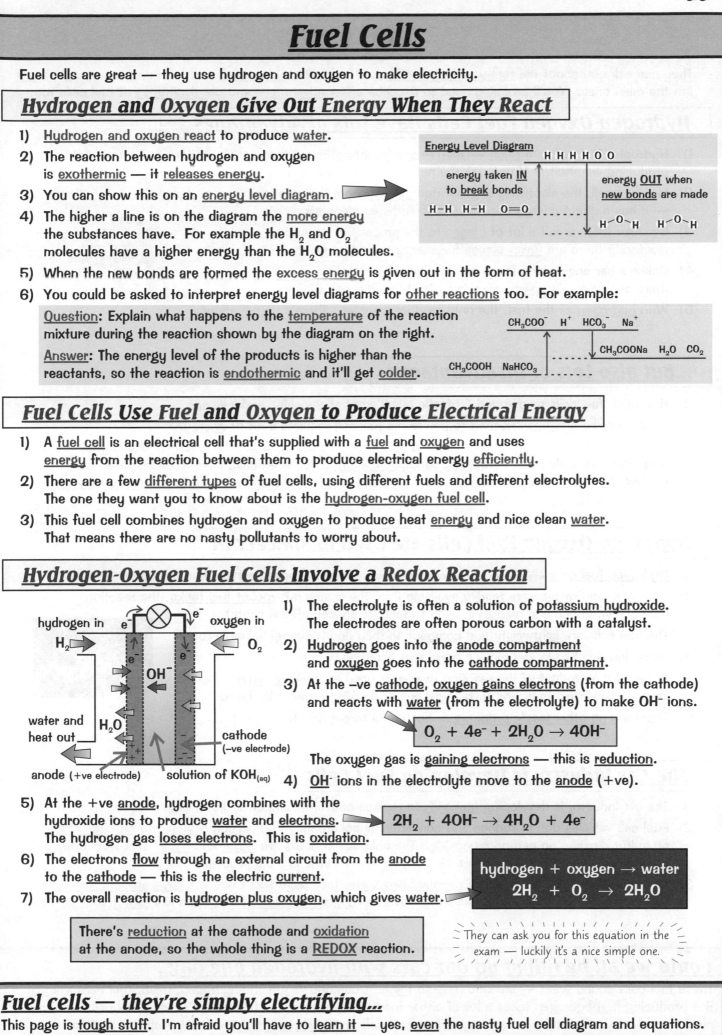

> Question: Explain what happens to the temperature of the reaction mixture during the reaction shown by the diagram on the right.
>
> Answer: The energy level of the products is higher than the reactants, so the reaction is endothermic and it'll get colder.

Fuel Cells Use Fuel and Oxygen to Produce Electrical Energy

1) A fuel cell is an electrical cell that's supplied with a fuel and oxygen and uses energy from the reaction between them to produce electrical energy efficiently.

2) There are a few different types of fuel cells, using different fuels and different electrolytes. The one they want you to know about is the hydrogen-oxygen fuel cell.

3) This fuel cell combines hydrogen and oxygen to produce heat energy and nice clean water. That means there are no nasty pollutants to worry about.

Hydrogen-Oxygen Fuel Cells Involve a Redox Reaction

1) The electrolyte is often a solution of potassium hydroxide. The electrodes are often porous carbon with a catalyst.

2) Hydrogen goes into the anode compartment and oxygen goes into the cathode compartment.

3) At the –ve cathode, oxygen gains electrons (from the cathode) and reacts with water (from the electrolyte) to make OH^- ions.

$$O_2 + 4e^- + 2H_2O \rightarrow 4OH^-$$

The oxygen gas is gaining electrons — this is reduction.

4) OH^- ions in the electrolyte move to the anode (+ve).

5) At the +ve anode, hydrogen combines with the hydroxide ions to produce water and electrons. The hydrogen gas loses electrons. This is oxidation.

$$2H_2 + 4OH^- \rightarrow 4H_2O + 4e^-$$

6) The electrons flow through an external circuit from the anode to the cathode — this is the electric current.

7) The overall reaction is hydrogen plus oxygen, which gives water.

> hydrogen + oxygen $\rightarrow$ water
> $$2H_2 + O_2 \rightarrow 2H_2O$$

There's reduction at the cathode and oxidation at the anode, so the whole thing is a REDOX reaction.

They can ask you for this equation in the exam — luckily it's a nice simple one.

Fuel cells — they're simply electrifying...

This page is tough stuff. I'm afraid you'll have to learn it — yes, even the nasty fuel cell diagram and equations.

Fuel Cells

They can ask you about the <u>real-world applications</u> of fuel cells. <u>Spacecraft</u> and (one day soon maybe) <u>cars</u> are the main ones. You'll probably need to describe a few <u>advantages</u> and <u>disadvantages</u> of fuel cells too.

Hydrogen-Oxygen Fuel Cells Have Lots of Advantages...

1) Hydrogen fuel cells are <u>great</u> — they're <u>much more efficient</u> than <u>power stations</u> or <u>batteries</u> at producing electricity. If you use the heat produced as well, their efficiency can be greater than <u>80%</u>.

2) In a <u>fuel cell</u>, the electricity is generated <u>directly</u> from the <u>reaction</u> — it has a direct energy transfer (so no turbines, generators, etc.).

3) Because there aren't a lot of <u>stages</u> to the process of generating electricity there are <u>fewer places</u> for energy to be <u>lost as heat</u>.

4) Unlike a car engine or a fossil fuel burning power station, there are <u>no moving parts</u>, so energy isn't lost through friction.

5) With <u>hydrogen</u> as the fuel, the only product is <u>water</u>. There's <u>no pollution</u>.

...But also Lots of Disadvantages

1) Hydrogen fuel cells may sound fantastic but it's not all sunshine and lollipops...

2) Producing the <u>hydrogen</u> needed to power the fuel cell requires a lot of <u>energy</u>. This energy may have come from burning non-renewable <u>fossil fuels</u> — which causes <u>pollution</u>.

3) Hydrogen fuel cells often contain <u>poisonous catalysts</u> which eventually have to be disposed of. Getting rid of the catalysts takes a lot of <u>time</u> and <u>money</u> and may cause <u>environmental problems</u>.

Hydrogen-Oxygen Fuel Cells are Used in Spacecraft

1) <u>Hydrogen fuel cells</u> are used to provide electrical power in <u>spacecraft</u> such as the Space Shuttle.

2) Hydrogen and oxygen are <u>readily available</u> from the spacecraft <u>rocket fuel tanks</u> (the reaction between hydrogen and oxygen is used to fuel the spacecraft's rockets).

3) The fuel cells are <u>lightweight</u> and <u>compact</u> so they don't take up valuable room.

4) They also don't have any <u>moving parts</u> that could go wrong.

5) Some of the product of the reaction (water) is used as <u>drinking water</u> — which saves the astronauts having to take gallons of drinking water with them.

6) There are <u>no other waste products</u> or pollutants to get rid of.

The Car Industry is Developing Fuel Cells

1) The car industry is developing <u>fuel cells</u> to replace conventional petrol/diesel engines.

2) Fuel cell vehicles don't produce any conventional pollutants — no <u>carbon dioxide</u>, no <u>nitrogen oxides</u>, no <u>sulfur dioxide</u>, no <u>carbon monoxide</u>. The only by-products are <u>water</u> and <u>heat</u>. This would be a major advantage in <u>cities</u>, where air pollution from traffic is a big problem.

3) As hydrogen can be obtained by <u>decomposing water</u> (see page 92) there is a <u>large amount available</u> for use as a fuel. This is a big advantage over using <u>non-renewable</u> fossil fuels like <u>petrol</u>.

Could we all be filling up our cars with hydrogen one day...

These fuel cells sound great — but you have to <u>think</u>. Once you've got the hydrogen, yeah, fuel cells are <u>ace</u>. But producing that hydrogen takes a lot of either fossil fuels or energy. That doesn't mean fuel cells won't be more important in the future, only that you need to look at the <u>whole picture</u> and weigh up the pros and cons.

CFCs and the Ozone Layer

Scientists <u>changed their minds</u> about CFCs as they found out more evidence about them.

At First Scientists Thought CFCs were Great...

1) <u>Chlorofluorocarbons</u> (CFCs for short) are <u>organic molecules</u> containing <u>carbon</u>, <u>chlorine</u> and <u>fluorine</u>, e.g. <u>dichlorodifluoromethane</u> CCl_2F_2 — this is like <u>methane</u> but with two chlorine and two fluorine atoms (and an extremely long name) instead of the four hydrogen atoms.

2) CFCs are <u>non-toxic</u>, <u>non-flammable</u> and chemically <u>inert</u> (unreactive). They're <u>insoluble</u> in water and have <u>low boiling points</u>. Scientists were very happy that they'd found some <u>non-toxic</u> and <u>inert</u> chemicals which were <u>ideal for many uses</u>.

3) Chlorofluorocarbons were used as <u>coolants</u> in <u>refrigerators</u> and <u>air-conditioning systems</u>.

4) CFCs were also used as <u>propellants</u> in <u>aerosol spray cans</u>.

...But Then They Discovered the Shocking Truth

> This is called the "hole in the ozone layer".

1) In 1974 scientists found that <u>chlorine</u> could help to <u>destroy ozone</u> (see equations on p98).

2) In 1985 scientists found <u>evidence</u> of <u>decreasing ozone levels</u> in the atmosphere over Antarctica.

3) Measurements in the upper atmosphere show high levels of compounds produced by the <u>breakdown of CFCs</u>. This supports the hypothesis that CFCs break down and destroy ozone.

4) Scientists are now <u>sure</u> that CFCs are linked to the depletion (thinning) of the ozone layer.

- <u>Ozone</u> is a form of oxygen with the formula O_3 — it has <u>three oxygen atoms</u> per molecule, unlike ordinary oxygen which has <u>two</u> atoms per molecule.
- It hangs about in the <u>ozone layer</u>, way up in the <u>stratosphere</u> (part of the upper atmosphere), doing the very important job of <u>absorbing ultraviolet (UV) light</u> from the Sun. Ozone absorbs UV light and breaks down into an <u>oxygen molecule</u> and an <u>oxygen atom</u>: O_3 + UV light $\rightarrow$ $O + O_2$ The oxygen molecule and oxygen atom join together to <u>make ozone again</u>: $O + O_2 \rightarrow O_3$
- <u>Reducing</u> the amount of <u>ozone</u> in the stratosphere results in <u>more UV light</u> passing through the atmosphere. Increased levels of <u>UV light</u> hitting the surface of the Earth can cause <u>medical problems</u> like increased risk of <u>sunburn</u> and <u>skin cancer</u>.

Some Countries Have Banned the Use of CFCs

1) Scientists' view that CFCs could damage the ozone layer caused a lot of <u>concern</u>.

2) But it took a while for society to do something about the mounting scientific evidence. Governments waited until the research had been thoroughly <u>peer reviewed</u> and <u>evaluated</u> before making a decision.

3) In 1978 the USA, Canada, Sweden and Norway <u>banned CFCs as aerosol propellants</u>.

4) After the <u>ozone hole</u> was discovered many countries (including the UK) got together and decided to reduce CFC production and eventually <u>ban CFCs completely</u>.

That's "chlorofluorocarbon" not "Chelsea Football Club"...

The ozone in the stratosphere is amazing stuff — it absorbs UV light and stops us from having to bear the full force of the Sun's UV output. Too much UV causes <u>sunburn</u> and <u>skin cancer</u>, so anything that damages the ozone and lets more UV through is a <u>bad</u> thing in the long run. So no more CFCs in fridges and spray cans.

CFCs and the Ozone Layer

CFCs damage ozone by forming <u>free radicals</u>. Learn what they are first, then how they attack ozone.

Free Radicals are Made by Breaking Covalent Bonds

1) A <u>covalent bond</u>, remember, is one where <u>two atoms share electrons</u> between them, like in H_2 (page 65).

2) A covalent bond can <u>break unevenly</u> to form <u>two ions</u>, e.g. $H–H \rightarrow H^+ + H^-$.
   The H^- has <u>both</u> of the shared electrons, and the poor old H^+ has <u>neither</u> of them.

3) But a covalent bond can also break <u>evenly</u> — and then <u>each atom</u> gets <u>one</u> of the shared electrons,
   e.g. $H–H \rightarrow H\cdot + H\cdot$ — the $H\cdot$ is called a <u>free radical</u>. (The unpaired electron is shown by a <u>dot</u>.)

4) The unpaired electron makes the free radical <u>very, very reactive</u>.

Chlorine Free Radicals from CFCs Damage the Ozone Layer

Learn these equations.

1) <u>Ultraviolet light</u> makes the carbon-chlorine bonds in CFCs break to form <u>free radicals</u>:

$$CCl_2F_2 \rightarrow CClF_2\cdot + Cl\cdot$$

2) This happens <u>high up in the atmosphere</u> (in the <u>stratosphere</u>),
   where the <u>ultraviolet light</u> from the Sun is <u>stronger</u>.

3) <u>Chlorine free radicals</u> from this reaction react with <u>ozone</u> (O_3),
   turning it into ordinary oxygen molecules (O_2) and chlorine oxide ($ClO\cdot$):

$$O_3 + Cl\cdot \rightarrow ClO\cdot + O_2$$

4) The chlorine oxide molecule is <u>very reactive</u>, and reacts with ozone
   to make two <u>oxygen molecules</u> and <u>another Cl· free radical</u>:

$$ClO\cdot + O_3 \rightarrow 2O_2 + Cl\cdot$$

5) This Cl· free radical now goes and reacts with <u>another ozone molecule</u>. This is a <u>chain reaction</u>, so just
   <u>one chlorine free radical</u> from one CFC molecule can go around breaking up <u>a lot of ozone molecules</u>.

> CFCs <u>don't attack ozone directly</u>. They break up and form chlorine atoms (chlorine free radicals)
> which attack ozone. The chlorine atoms <u>aren't used up</u>, so they can carry on breaking down ozone.

CFCs Stay in the Stratosphere for Ages

1) CFCs are <u>not very reactive</u> and will only react with one or two chemicals that are present in the
   atmosphere. And they'll only break up to form <u>chlorine atoms</u> in the stratosphere, where there's
   plenty of high-energy ultraviolet light around. They won't do it in the lower atmosphere.

2) This means that the CFCs in the stratosphere now will take a <u>long time</u> to be removed.

3) Remember, each CFC molecule produces one chlorine atom which can react with an <u>awful lot</u> of
   ozone molecules. <u>Thousands</u> of them, in fact.

4) So the millions of CFC molecules that are present in the stratosphere will continue to destroy
   ozone for a long time — even <u>after all CFCs have been banned</u>. Each molecule will <u>stay around</u>
   for a long time, and each molecule will <u>destroy a lot of ozone</u> molecules.

Alkanes and HFCs are Safe Alternatives to CFCs

1) Alkanes <u>don't react</u> with ozone, so they can provide a safe alternative to CFCs.

2) <u>Hydrofluorocarbons</u> (<u>HFCs</u>) are compounds very similar to CFCs — but they contain <u>no chlorine</u>.
   It's the chlorine in CFCs that attacks ozone, remember.

3) Scientists have investigated the compounds that could be produced by breakdown of HFCs in the upper
   atmosphere, and <u>none of them</u> seem to be able to <u>attack ozone</u>. <u>Evidence suggests</u> HFCs are <u>safe</u>.

Oooh, here comes the tricky science bit...

Here's the deal — <u>yes</u>, you do need to know what a free radical is, and <u>yes</u> you do need to learn the equations
for the reaction between chlorine atoms and ozone. You can't just glide your eyes over the equations and hope
for the best. <u>Cover the page and scribble them down</u>, then check what you wrote. It'll be worth it in the end.

Hardness of Water

Water where you live might be <u>hard</u> or <u>soft</u>. It depends on the <u>rocks</u> your water meets on its way to you.

Hard Water Makes Scum and Scale

1) <u>Hard water</u> won't easily form a <u>lather</u> with soap. It makes a <u>nasty scum</u> instead. So to get a decent lather you need to use <u>more soap</u> or <u>softer water</u>.

2) Hard water also forms <u>limescale</u> (calcium carbonate) on the insides of pipes, boilers and kettles. <u>Limescale</u> is a <u>thermal insulator</u>. This means that a <u>kettle</u> with <u>limescale on the heating element</u> takes <u>longer to boil</u> than a <u>clean</u> non-scaled-up kettle. Scale can even <u>eventually block pipes</u>.

Hardness is Caused by Ca²⁺ and Mg²⁺ Ions

Hard water contains <u>calcium ions</u> (Ca^{2+}), <u>magnesium ions</u> (Mg^{2+}), or both. As water flows over rocks and through soils containing calcium and magnesium compounds, these ions dissolve in it.

1) <u>Magnesium sulfate</u> ($MgSO_4$) dissolves in water — and so does calcium sulfate ($CaSO_4$) (though only a little bit).

2) <u>Calcium carbonate</u> commonly exists as chalk, limestone or marble. It doesn't dissolve in water, but it will react with <u>acids</u>. And since <u>CO_2</u> from the air <u>dissolves in rainwater</u> (forming <u>carbonic acid</u>, $CO_2 + H_2O \rightarrow H_2CO_3$), rainwater is slightly <u>acidic</u>. This means that calcium carbonate can react with rainwater to form <u>calcium hydrogencarbonate</u> ($H_2CO_3 + CaCO_3 \rightarrow Ca(HCO_3)_2$), which is <u>soluble</u>.

Overall the <u>equation</u> for the reaction is:

> carbon dioxide + water + calcium carbonate → calcium hydrogencarbonate

Temporary Hardness Can be Removed by Boiling

There are two kinds of hardness — <u>temporary</u> and <u>permanent</u>.
Temporary hardness is caused by the <u>hydrogencarbonate</u> ion, <u>HCO_3^-</u>, in $Ca(HCO_3)_2$.
Hardness caused by dissolved <u>calcium sulfate</u> (among other things) is <u>permanent hardness</u>.

1) <u>Temporary hardness</u> is removed by <u>boiling</u>. The calcium hydrogencarbonate <u>decomposes</u> to form insoluble $CaCO_3$. This <u>won't work</u> for permanent hardness, though. Heating a <u>sulfate</u> ion does <u>nowt</u>. (This calcium carbonate precipitate is the 'limescale' on your kettle — it's <u>insoluble</u>.)

> calcium hydrogencarbonate → calcium carbonate + water + carbon dioxide
> $Ca(HCO_3)_2(aq) \rightarrow CaCO_3(s) + H_2O(l) + CO_2(g)$

2) <u>Both types of hardness</u> are removed by adding washing soda — <u>sodium carbonate</u>, Na_2CO_3. The carbonate ions join onto the calcium ions and make an <u>insoluble precipitate</u> of calcium carbonate. This works whether the hardness is due to calcium sulfate or calcium hydrogencarbonate.

> $Ca^{2+}(aq) + CO_3^{2-}(aq) \rightarrow CaCO_3(s)$

3) <u>Both types of hardness</u> can also be removed by '<u>ion exchange resin</u>'. This clever bit of chemistry has lots of <u>sodium ions</u> (or <u>hydrogen ions</u>) and 'exchanges' them for calcium or magnesium ions.

Ice is fairly hard, come to think of it...

One thing that I've never understood is that they sell water softeners in areas that <u>already</u> have soft water. Hmm... For the exam, you're supposed to know how the calcium and magnesium salts that cause hard water <u>get into</u> the water in the first place, and how they can be <u>removed</u>. So make sure you know it.

Hardness of Water

In <u>hard water areas</u>, you need much <u>more soap</u> to get a <u>nice lather</u> as you wash your hands. At some point in the past, someone noticed this — and decided to design a <u>test</u> to show exactly <u>how hard</u> or <u>soft</u> your water is.

An Experiment to Compare the Hardness of Water Samples

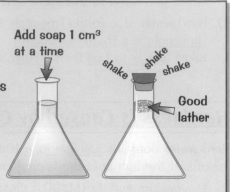

<u>METHOD</u>:

1) Add <u>100 cm³ of water</u> to a <u>conical flask</u>.

2) Add <u>1 cm³ soap solution</u> to the water. Put a <u>bung</u> in and <u>shake</u>.

3) Repeat this until a <u>good lasting lather</u> is formed. (A lasting lather is one where the <u>bubbles cover the surface</u> for <u>at least 30 seconds</u>.)

4) <u>Record</u> how much soap was needed.

Add soap 1 cm³ at a time

shake shake shake

Good lather

This method was carried out on <u>3 different samples of water</u> — <u>distilled</u> water, <u>local tap</u> water and <u>imported tap</u> water.

<u>Fresh samples</u> of each type of water were then <u>boiled</u>, and the experiment was <u>repeated</u>.

Here's the <u>TABLE OF RESULTS</u>:

Sample	Volume of soap solution needed to give a good lather	
	using unboiled water in cm³	using boiled water in cm³
Distilled	1	1
Local water	7	1
Imported water	14	8

The results tell you the following things about the water:

1) Distilled water contains little or no <u>hardness</u> — only the <u>minimum</u> amount of soap was needed.

2) The <u>imported water</u> contains <u>more hardness</u> than <u>local water</u> — <u>more soap</u> was needed to produce a lather.

3) The local water contains only <u>temporary hardness</u> — all the hardness is <u>removed by boiling</u>. You can tell because the same amount of soap was needed for <u>boiled local water</u> as for <u>distilled water</u>.

4) The imported water contains both <u>temporary</u> and <u>permanent hardness</u>. 8 cm³ of soap is still needed to produce a lather after boiling.

5) If your brain's really switched on, you'll see that the local water and the imported water contain the <u>same amount</u> of <u>temporary hardness</u>. In both cases, the amount of soap needed in the <u>boiled</u> sample is <u>6 cm³ less</u> than in the <u>unboiled</u> sample.

My dad's water is harder than your dad's water...

Sigh. Anyhow, the usual message here. There <u>is</u> an exam coming up, and <u>any</u> of this hard water stuff could be on it, including interpreting results. Read through experimental data carefully — don't drop any easy marks.

Alcohols

There's a whole group of compounds called <u>alcohols</u>, and they're rather useful to industrial chemists.

Alcohols Have an '-OH' Functional Group and End in '-ol'

1) The <u>general formula</u> of an alcohol is $C_nH_{2n+1}OH$.

2) So if an alcohol has <u>2 carbons</u> (n = 2), its formula will be $C_2H_{(2\times2)+1}OH$, which is <u>C_2H_5OH</u>.

3) The basic <u>naming</u> system is the same as for alkanes (see p.19) — but replace the final '<u>-e</u>' with '<u>-ol</u>'.

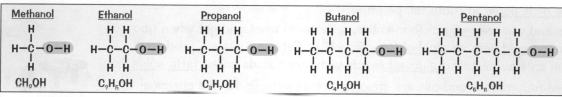

Fermentation Produces Ethanol

1) Fermentation is used to convert <u>sugars</u> (usually a glucose solution) into <u>ethanol</u>.

> glucose → ethanol + carbon dioxide
> $C_6H_{12}O_6 \rightarrow 2C_2H_5OH + 2CO_2$

2) The reaction is brought about by <u>enzymes</u> (biological catalysts) found in <u>yeasts</u>.

3) The <u>temperature</u> needs to be <u>carefully controlled</u>. If it's <u>too cold</u> the yeast is inactive, so the reaction's really <u>slow</u> — but if it's <u>too hot</u> the enzymes in the yeast are <u>denatured</u> (destroyed). The reaction's carried out at an optimum (ideal) temperature between 25 °C and 50 °C.

4) It's also important to prevent <u>oxygen</u> getting at the alcohol. This is because oxygen converts <u>ethanol</u> to <u>ethanoic acid</u> (which is what you get in <u>vinegar</u>).

5) Once the reaction stops the mixture can be distilled using <u>fractional distillation</u> to give pure ethanol.

Ethanol Can Also be Made by Hydrating Ethene

1) This is how ethanol is usually made <u>industrially</u>.

2) <u>Ethene</u> (C_2H_4) will react with <u>steam</u> (H_2O) to make <u>ethanol</u>.

> ethene + water (steam) → ethanol

3) The reaction needs a <u>temperature</u> of 300 °C and a <u>pressure</u> of 70 atmospheres. To speed up the reaction the ethene and steam are passed over a heated <u>phosphoric acid catalyst</u>.

> $C_2H_4 + H_2O \rightarrow C_2H_5OH$

Fermentation vs Hydration

In the exam you may be asked to <u>compare</u> the two methods of producing ethanol.

<u>Manufacture</u>: Fermentation is usually a <u>batch</u> process which is slow and inefficient. Ethene hydration uses a <u>continuous</u> process so the ethanol is made more quickly. Hydration requires much harsher reaction <u>conditions</u> so is a more <u>expensive</u> process to run.

<u>Sustainability</u>: The ethanol made by fermentation is a <u>renewable fuel</u>. It's made from renewable resources (e.g. sugar cane or sugar beets), so we <u>won't run out</u>. The ethene produced in the hydration reaction is a <u>non-renewable fuel</u>. It's produced from <u>crude oil</u>, which will one day <u>run out</u>.

<u>Purity</u>: The ethanol made by fermentation <u>isn't very pure</u> and has to be purified by distillation before it's used. The ethanol made by hydration is of a much <u>higher purity</u>.

<u>Atom Economy</u>: Fermentation has a <u>lower atom economy</u> than hydration as not all of the atoms in the reactants are used to make the ethanol (for more on atom economy see page 53).

<u>Percentage yield</u>: The yield of a hydration reaction is very low but by <u>recycling</u> any unused reactants you can achieve yields of up to 95%. The yields achieved by using fermentation are <u>much lower</u>.

---

300 °C, 70 atm, acid — why don't home brewers hydrate ethene...

Learn the equations for the <u>hydration of ethene</u> and the <u>fermentation of ethanol</u>. They're both very important reactions.

Fats and Oils

Lard, glorious lard! Hot butter and blubber...

Fats and Oils Come from Animals or Plants

1) Animal fats and oils include <u>lard</u> (pork fat), <u>blubber</u> (whale fat), <u>ghee</u> (butter oil) and <u>cod liver oil</u>.

2) Plant fats and oils include <u>walnut oil</u>, <u>coconut oil</u>, <u>olive oil</u> and <u>soya oil</u>.

3) <u>Fats are solid</u> and <u>oils are liquid</u> at <u>room temperature</u>. For example, <u>lard is solid</u> at room temperature, <u>olive oil is liquid</u> at room temperature.

4) Fats and oils are <u>esters</u>. Remember, an ester is what you get when you react an <u>acid</u> with an <u>alcohol</u> (see page 12). Fats and oils are produced when an alcohol called <u>glycerol</u> reacts with some acids called <u>fatty acids</u>.

5) These natural fats and oils are <u>important raw materials</u> for the <u>chemical industry</u> — e.g. in paints, machine lubricants, detergents and cosmetics. They can be used as alternatives to chemicals made from <u>crude oil</u>.

Emulsions Can be Made from Oil and Water

1) Oils <u>don't mix in water</u> — they're <u>immiscible</u>.

2) However, you <u>can</u> mix immiscible liquids like oil and water to make an <u>emulsion</u>. You have to <u>shake</u> the two liquids <u>vigorously</u>. This'll break up the oil into very small droplets which disperse through the water.

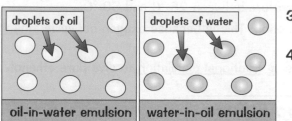

droplets of oil

droplets of water

oil-in-water emulsion   water-in-oil emulsion

3) <u>Milk</u> is an <u>oil-in-water emulsion</u> (oil droplets suspended in water). There's less oil than water.

4) <u>Butter</u> is a <u>water-in-oil emulsion</u> (water droplets suspended in oil). There's more oil than water.

Vegetable Oils Can be Used to Produce Biodiesel

1) Vegetable oils such as rapeseed oil and soybean oil can be <u>processed</u> and turned into <u>fuels</u>.

2) Vegetable oil provides a lot of <u>energy</u> — that's why it's suitable for use as a fuel.

3) A particularly useful fuel made from vegetable oils is called <u>biodiesel</u>. Biodiesel has similar properties to <u>ordinary diesel fuel</u> — it burns in the same way, so you can use it as an <u>alternative</u> to diesel fuel.

Fats and Oils are Used to Make Soaps

1) Vegetable oils react with alkali to make <u>soap</u>.

2) Natural fats and oils are boiled up with sodium hydroxide. The <u>hot sodium hydroxide</u> splits up the fats and oils to produce a <u>soap</u> and <u>glycerol</u>.

3) This process is called <u>saponification</u>. Yes, yet another long chemistry word.

4) The chemical reaction first breaks up the fat or oil to release glycerol and fatty acids. This is called <u>hydrolysis</u> (it means "breaking apart with water"). Then the fatty acids react with the sodium hydroxide to make <u>soap</u>.

Learn the <u>word equation</u>: ➡   fat   +   sodium hydroxide   →   soap + glycerol

A pint of milk fell on my head — I was overcome with emulsion...

Hundreds of years ago they used to make soap mainly from <u>animal fat</u>. Today <u>vegetable fats</u> and <u>oils</u> are used as well — e.g. palm oil and olive oil, as in Palmolive®. I'm pretty sure the animals are dead chuffed.

Using Plant Oils

Oils are quite runny at room temperature. That's fine for salad dressing, say, but not so good for spreading in your sandwiches. For that, you could <u>hydrogenate</u> the oil to make <u>margarine</u>...

Unsaturated Oils Contain C=C Double Bonds

1) Oils and fats contain <u>long-chain molecules</u> with lots of <u>carbon</u> atoms.

2) They can be either <u>saturated</u> or <u>unsaturated</u>.

3) Saturated oils and fats only have <u>single C-C bonds</u>.

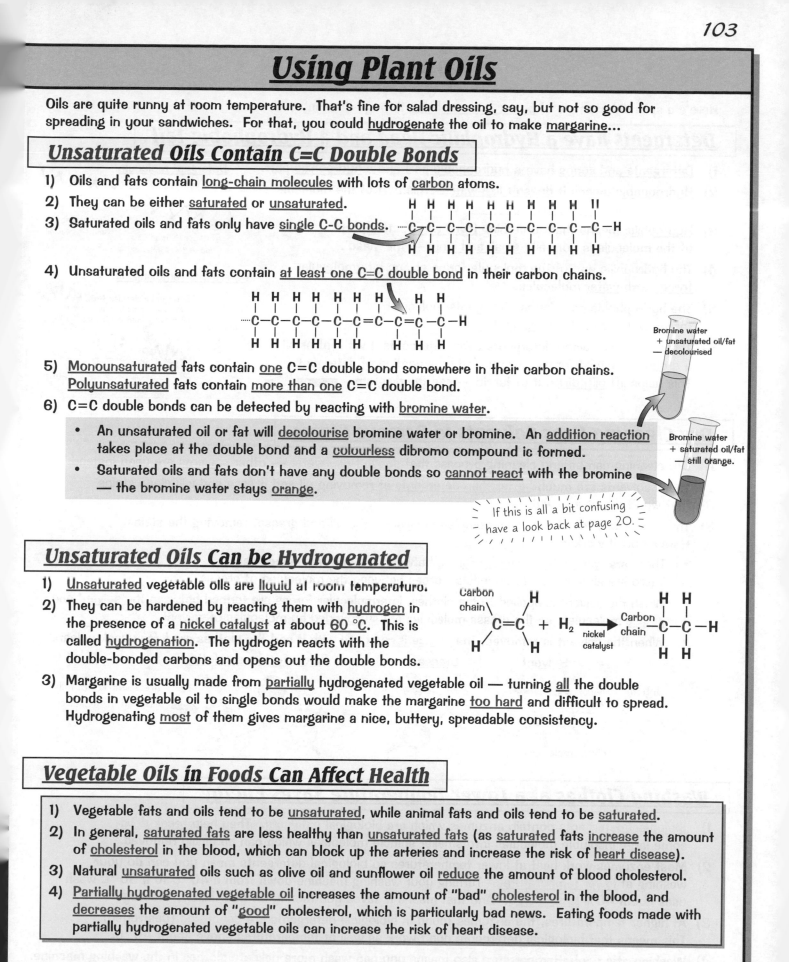

4) Unsaturated oils and fats contain <u>at least one C=C double bond</u> in their carbon chains.

5) <u>Monounsaturated</u> fats contain <u>one</u> C=C double bond somewhere in their carbon chains. <u>Polyunsaturated</u> fats contain <u>more than one</u> C=C double bond.

6) C=C double bonds can be detected by reacting with <u>bromine water</u>.

- An unsaturated oil or fat will <u>decolourise</u> bromine water or bromine. An <u>addition reaction</u> takes place at the double bond and a <u>colourless</u> dibromo compound is formed.
- Saturated oils and fats don't have any double bonds so <u>cannot react</u> with the bromine — the bromine water stays <u>orange</u>.

Bromine water + unsaturated oil/fat — decolourised

Bromine water + saturated oil/fat — still orange.

If this is all a bit confusing have a look back at page 20.

Unsaturated Oils Can be Hydrogenated

1) <u>Unsaturated</u> vegetable oils are <u>liquid</u> at room temperature.

2) They can be hardened by reacting them with <u>hydrogen</u> in the presence of a <u>nickel catalyst</u> at about <u>60 °C</u>. This is called <u>hydrogenation</u>. The hydrogen reacts with the double-bonded carbons and opens out the double bonds.

3) Margarine is usually made from <u>partially</u> hydrogenated vegetable oil — turning <u>all</u> the double bonds in vegetable oil to single bonds would make the margarine <u>too hard</u> and difficult to spread. Hydrogenating <u>most</u> of them gives margarine a nice, buttery, spreadable consistency.

Vegetable Oils in Foods Can Affect Health

1) Vegetable fats and oils tend to be <u>unsaturated</u>, while animal fats and oils tend to be <u>saturated</u>.

2) In general, <u>saturated fats</u> are less healthy than <u>unsaturated fats</u> (as <u>saturated</u> fats <u>increase</u> the amount of <u>cholesterol</u> in the blood, which can block up the arteries and increase the risk of <u>heart disease</u>).

3) Natural <u>unsaturated</u> oils such as olive oil and sunflower oil <u>reduce</u> the amount of blood cholesterol.

4) <u>Partially hydrogenated vegetable oil</u> increases the amount of "bad" <u>cholesterol</u> in the blood, and <u>decreases</u> the amount of "<u>good</u>" cholesterol, which is particularly bad news. Eating foods made with partially hydrogenated vegetable oils can increase the risk of heart disease.

Double bonds — licensed to saturate...

This is tricky stuff. In a nutshell... there are <u>saturated</u> and <u>unsaturated</u> fats and you can test for them using bromine. By reacting unsaturated fats with <u>hydrogen</u> you give them more single bonds — this makes 'em more spreadable. And finally, unsaturated fats tend to be better for you because they're <u>less likely</u> to cause clotting in your arteries. Phew.

Detergents

Here's a splendid example of <u>better, cleaner living</u> through Chemistry.

Detergents have a Hydrophilic Head and a Hydrophobic Tail

1) <u>Detergents and soaps</u> have a <u>hydrophobic</u> part and a <u>hydrophilic</u> part.

2) <u>Hydrophobic</u> means it <u>doesn't like water</u>. This part of the molecule is normally a <u>long hydrocarbon chain</u> or 'tail'.

3) <u>Hydrophilic</u> means that something <u>loves water</u>. This part of the molecule is normally <u>small and ionic</u> — the 'head'.

4) The hydrophilic end of the molecule forms strong <u>intermolecular forces</u> with <u>water</u> molecules.

5) The hydrophobic part forms strong intermolecular forces with molecules of <u>oil and fat</u>.

6) This means that when detergents come into contact with fat or oil a <u>droplet</u> of oil/fat forms, surrounded by a coating of detergent. This helps <u>lift oily dirt</u> out of fabric — see the diagram.

Detergent molecule
hydrophilic 'head'
end — loves water
hydrophobic 'tail'
end — loves oil

Detergents removing oil
Detergent molecules surround the oil blob and lift it away from the fabric
Water molecules
Oil stain on clothes
Fabric

Dry Cleaning Uses Solvents to Remove Stains

1) Dry cleaning can be <u>any</u> cleaning process that <u>doesn't use water</u> — other <u>solvents</u> are used instead.

2) These solvents are much <u>better than detergents</u> at removing oil and grease and will clean stains that won't dissolve in water.

3) This is because the solvent can completely <u>dissolve</u> the oil and grease, removing the stains. Here's how it works:

- There are <u>weak intermolecular forces</u> between the solvent molecules. There are also weak intermolecular forces between the molecules of grease.

- When the solvent is applied to the clothes, intermolecular forces are formed <u>between</u> the <u>solvent</u> and <u>grease</u> molecules, so the grease molecules are <u>surrounded</u> by molecules of solvent.

- When the solvent is removed, the <u>grease is removed</u> with it and the clothes are left squeaky clean.

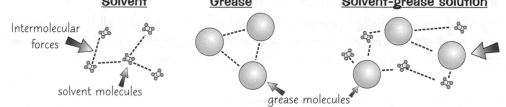

Solvent
Intermolecular forces
solvent molecules

Grease
grease molecules

Solvent-grease solution
grease molecules fully dissolved in the solvent

Washing Clothes at a Lower Temperature Saves Energy

1) <u>Biological detergents</u> contain enzymes which are biological <u>catalysts</u>. They help <u>break down</u> some large insoluble molecules into smaller soluble molecules which can be easily removed.

2) Most enzymes work best at lower temperatures so biological detergents mean you can do your washing at <u>lower temperatures</u>. Turning your washing machine down from a 40 °C to a 30 °C wash uses about 40% <u>less energy</u>. And that means it saves you money on your bills... Hooray.

3) At higher temperatures, the enzymes found in biological detergents are <u>denatured</u> (destroyed). This means that biological detergents don't work as well at temperatures above about 40 °C.

4) Washing at a <u>cooler temperature</u> also means you can wash more <u>delicate clothes</u> in the washing machine.

Detergents and solvents — what a washout...

Pretty neat don't cha think... Well, maybe not but you've still got to learn it. There's quite a lot to get your head around on this page, so make sure you know how <u>detergents</u> work and also how <u>dry cleaning solvents</u> work. And remember that washing your clothes at a lower temperature can <u>save energy</u> and <u>money</u>.

Revision Summary for Module C6

Time to test yourself. If you can't answer these now, you won't be able to answer them in the exam. But this is the end of the book. So when you've done these you can just sit back and wait for your exam. Well, you could... but that would be silly. You need to keep your brain in the chemistry mood all the way through to the exam — don't let any of that hard-earned knowledge just dribble away. A few days before the exam, come and try all these questions again. Just to check you've still got what it takes.

1) Fill in the gaps: A loss of electrons is _____. A gain of electrons is _____.

2) Give a symbol half-equation for the oxidation of Fe^{2+} to Fe^{3+}.

3) What is a displacement reaction?

4) Give the word equation for the rusting of iron.

5) Explain how greasing and painting protect against rust.

6) Why isn't it always a good plan to buy dented cans of beans?

7) An oil drilling platform uses sacrificial protection. What's "sacrificial protection"?

8) Why is hydrogen released during the electrolysis of $H_2SO_4(aq)$?

9) Write the half-equations at each electrode for the electrolysis of $PbI_2(l)$.

10) Describe two ways in which you could increase the amount of product made during electrolysis.

11)* If 2 amps of current flows for 3 seconds, how much charge is that, in coulombs?

12) Sketch an energy level diagram for the reaction between hydrogen and oxygen.

13) Give the definition of a fuel cell.

14) Write down the overall reaction in an hydrogen-oxygen fuel cell.

15) Give two advantages of hydrogen fuel cells over conventional ways of generating electricity

16) Give an advantage of hydrogen fuel cells as a power source in a spacecraft.

17) Why is the car industry researching fuel cells?

18) Why were CFCs initially popular?

19) What's the name for the part of the upper atmosphere that contains the ozone layer?

20) How are free radicals formed?

21) Write an equation for the reaction between ozone and chlorine atoms.

22) One CFC molecule can destroy thousands of ozone molecules. Why is this?

23) Is water hardness caused by calcium sulfate permanent or temporary?

24)* A sample of water requires a large amount of soap to give a good lather both when it is unboiled and after it is boiled. What type of hardness does it have — none, temporary or permanent?

25) What's the general formula for alcohols?

26) What's the optimum temperature range for fermentation?

27) Compare the sustainability of ethene hydration and fermentation of sugars.

28) Are fats and oils: a) alkanes, b) alcohols, c) esters?

29) Write down a word equation for saponification.

30) How would you test margarine to see if it's saturated or unsaturated?

31) Which are healthier, saturated or unsaturated fats?

32) What does hydrophilic mean? What does hydrophobic mean?

33) Describe how solvents remove stains.

* Answers on page 108.

Index

Index

Index and Answers

Answers

Revision Summary for Module C1 (page 29)

1)   14 H and 6 C

2)

$$H - \underset{\underset{H}{|}}{\overset{\overset{H}{|}}{C}} - \underset{\underset{H}{|}}{\overset{\overset{H}{|}}{C}} - \underset{\underset{H}{|}}{\overset{\overset{H}{|}}{C}} - H$$

4) $2Na + 2H_2O \rightarrow 2NaOH + H_2$

34) E.g. $C_2H_6 + 3O_2 \rightarrow CO + CO_2 + 3H_2O$

Revision Summary for Module C2 (page 45)

28) phosphoric acid + potassium hydroxide → potassium phosphate + water

29) $H_2SO_4 + Na_2CO_3 \rightarrow Na_2SO_4 + H_2O + CO_2$

Revision Summary for Module C3 (page 57)

10) When using the concentrated acid it will take less time to produce the same amount of gas than when using the dilute acid — the rate of reaction is faster. The slope of the graph (time vs volume of gas) will be steeper for the acid which produces the faster rate of reaction.

11) a) 40
     b) 108
     c) $12 + (16 \times 2) = 44$
     d) $24 + 12 + (16 \times 3) = 84$
     e) $27 + 3 \times (16 + 1) = 78$
     f) $65 + 16 = 81$
     g) $(23 \times 2) + 12 + (16 \times 3) = 106$
     h) $23 + 35.5 = 58.5$

12) a) 186.8 g
     b) 80.3 g
     c) 20.1 g

Revision Summary for Module C4 (page 73)

24) a) bromine + lithium   →   lithium bromide
         Br_2 + 2Li   →   2LiBr
     b) chlorine + potassium →   potassium chloride
         Cl_2 + 2K   →   2KCl
     c) iodine   + sodium   →   sodium iodide
         I_2 + 2Na   →   2NaI

Bottom of page 75

1)   a) CH_2
     b) CH_2O
     c) $AlCl_3$

2) $\quad$ C $\qquad\qquad\qquad$ H
     $\quad$ 2.4 $\qquad\qquad\quad$ 0.8
     $2.4 \div 12 = 0.2 \qquad 0.8 \div 1 = 0.8$
     $\quad$ 2 $\qquad\qquad\qquad$ 8
     So the empirical formula is CH_4

Bottom of page 79

number of moles of $H_2SO_4 = 0.2 \times (25 \div 1000) = 0.005$
$H_2SO_4 + Ca(OH)_2 \rightarrow CaSO_4 + 2H_2O$
So for every mole of H_2SO_4 there is one mole of $Ca(OH)_2$
So the number of moles of $Ca(OH)_2 = 0.005$
concentration = moles ÷ volume $= 0.005 \div (40 \div 1000)$
$= 0.005 \div 0.04 = 0.125$ mol/dm³

Revision Summary for Module C5 (page 89)

2) M_r of $Na_2SO_4 = (23 \times 2) + 32 + (16 \times 4) = 142$
     moles = mass ÷ $M_r = 284 \div 142 = 2$
3) M_r of Cl_2 in $MgCl_2 = 35.5 \times 2 = 71$
     mass = moles × $M_r = 2 \times 71 = 142$ g
5)   Number of moles of $Na_2O = 108.2 \div 62 = 1.745$
     4 moles of Na produce 2 moles of Na_2O.
     So number of moles of Na $= 1.745 \times 2 = 3.49$
     mass = moles × $M_r = 3.49 \times 23 = 80.3$ g
6) $\quad$ Mg $\qquad\qquad\qquad$ S $\qquad\qquad\qquad$ O
     $\quad$ 21.9 $\qquad\qquad\quad$ 29.3 $\qquad\qquad\quad$ 58.3
     $21.9 \div 24 = 0.9 \quad 29.3 \div 32 = 0.9 \quad 58.3 \div 16 = 3.6$
     $\quad$ 9 $\qquad\qquad\qquad$ 9 $\qquad\qquad\qquad$ 36
     $\quad$ 1 $\qquad\qquad\qquad$ 1 $\qquad\qquad\qquad$ 4
     So the empirical formula is $MgSO_4$
7)   a) 7.5 g/dm³
     b) $7.5 \div 2 = 3.75$ g/dm³
8) $0.2 \times (500 \div 1000) = 0.1$ moles
9)   Take 50 cm³ of the 1 mol/dm³ sulfuric acid solution, and dilute it with 200 cm³ of water.
14) a) $0.15 \times (25 \div 1000)$
         $= 0.00375 \,(3.75 \times 10^{-3})$ moles of KOH
         $HNO_3 + KOH \rightarrow KNO_3 + H_2O$
         1 mole of nitric acid reacts with
         1 mole of potassium hydroxide
         concentration $= 0.00375 \div (22.5 \div 1000)$
         $= 0.167$ mol/dm³
     b) mass = moles × $M_r = 0.167 \times (1 + 14 + (16 \times 3))$
         $= 10.5$ g/dm³
18) a) 50 cm³
     b) about 13 s

Revision Summary for Module C6 (page 105)

11) $Q = I \times t = 2 \times 3 = 6$ C
24) permanent hardness